almost ZERO CARB CARB FAT FAST

LowCarbeDiem.com

ANN MOORE

DEDICATION

Thank you, Mom and Dad, for encouraging my artist nature, for believing in my wild ideas and supporting everything creative in my life. Thank you for the childhood French Quarter plays, and the freedom to explore countless projects from cardboard boxes (without objection). Thank you for my deep blue sea.

I'd also like to thank the Mom I've never met, for placing me in such wonderful hands.

I'm more grateful than I could ever express.

TABLE OF CONTENTS

Shortbread Cookies

SURPRISE!

To thank you for your generous support, I made cookies.

Yes, they're almost zero carb.

Here's the last keto cookie recipe you'll ever need and 7 juicy ways to use your fasting plan.

7 Ways to Use Your Fast

The *Almost Zero Carb Fat Fast* is a stall-breaker, scale-mover, energy booster, rescue after a slip, and a way to enter deep ketosis quickly or train your body to eat less every day.

Yes, your plan does a lot. And it does it well.

- Use your fasting recipes before a "cheat day" or special occasion.

- Follow the fast once (or twice) each month to keep your metabolism guessing.

- Add your fast one day a week and avoid plateau.

- Complete a mini weekend fast if you need energy, or if your progress feels slow.

- Eat these recipes anytime in larger portions, and free up some carbs for your day/week.

- Follow the fast for a full five days and reach a deeper state of ketosis.

- Make your fast a go-to method for losing "those last 10 pounds."

SHORTBREAD "THANK YOU" COOKIES

0.66g net carbs per cookie - 164 calories
Servings: 12 Cookies

This is your signature, base cookie ready for extras like chopped nuts, flavored extracts, espresso, sugar-free Jello powder mixes, toasted coconut, nut butters, cocoa powder, mashed berries, dark chocolate, citrus zest, grated cheese/veggies, spices/herbs or bacon.

INGREDIENTS

8 tbsp salted butter, softened

pinch of salt

2/3 c granulated erythritol (or equiv of sweetener like stevia)

1/2 tsp almond extract

1 tsp vanilla extract

2 c almond flour, superfine

(or sift)

METHOD

Preheat oven to 350 F.

Beat butter, salt and sweetener until fluffy. Add almond and vanilla extracts, blending well.

Add almond flour and beat until just blended, forming a stiff dough.

Divide dough into balls and press flat using a spatula or bottom of a glass.

Place on a parchment paper-lined baking sheet and bake for 15 minutes.

Remove and let cool completely before eating for maximum crunch.

For softer cookies, remove from oven after 13 minutes.

Add toppings right when cookies come out of the oven and are still warm.

NOTE: *The nutrition stats below are for total recipe AND per serving. Number of servings varies due to personal preference (making a few large cookies, or smaller button cookies).*

Total Recipe: 1973 Calories; 188g Fat (85.3% calories from fat); 41g Protein; 32g Carbohydrate; 24g Dietary Fiber.
Per Serving: 164 Calories; 16g Fat (85.3% calories from fat); 3g Protein; 3g Carbohydrate; 2.34g Dietary Fiber.

"Never mistake motion for action."
- E. Hemingway

MOST-ASKED QUESTIONS

What is this Fast, exactly?

The *Almost Zero Carb Fat Fast* is based on the *Atkins Fat Fast* and the zero carb diet, both of which let you reach deep ketosis in record time. The fat loss is incredible and the plan is highly effective for breaking stalls and preventing plateau.

During this fat fast, calories are limited and macronutrient ratios must be within certain parameters - that is, each recipe has very specific percentages of fat, carbs and protein so you'll burn the most stored body fat in the shortest amount of time.

Why is this Fast better than others?

Hitting a diet plateau is one of our most frustrating low carb issues, especially when we're doing everything "by the books." Enter fat fasts: the go-to favorite for breaking through quickly. The *Almost Zero* fasting plan is a modified version of a 3 to 5 day fat fast. This fast helps you keep muscle tone, and lets you eat more calories each day.

This fasting plan is also easier to complete, with full breakfasts, lunches, snacks, soups, salads, dinners and desserts... plus specialty drinks, sauces and dips.

This plan is very short and extremely aggressive, but you only need to follow it a few days. Then simply enjoy the recipes any time after your fast is complete, without limiting your servings/portions.

How much fat will I lose?

Fat loss depends on your current weight and body fat percentage. Low carbers with more weight and a higher body fat percentage lose more than those with just a few extra pounds.

On average, if you follow this fast for 3 days, expect to lose 6 to 9 pounds. If you follow the fast for 5 days, your weight loss could be 8 to 15 pounds (or more).

Once you go back to your regular way of eating, some of the water weight lost during the plan returns (20% on average). This is normal, since deep ketosis quickly eliminates excess water stored in the body. Increasing your net carbs slowly after the plan (adding special transition days) helps keep this water weight from returning.

What's so fabulous about these recipes?

Of course, there's plenty of info available online about fat fasts, so the real value is the decadent variety of the *Almost Zero* recipes, their ultimate versatility and their special macros. This fasting plan is worth it for the recipes alone, whether you decide to use it as a stall breaker, ketosis-starter, energizer, fat-burner or just free up some carbs for the day/week.

It's very difficult to find great-tasting recipes with almost no carbs. BAM! You just nabbed an entire book. The recipes in your fast are super high fat versions of very popular low carb and keto recipes (easy favorites).

These workhorse recipes are designed with very specific keto macros that burn fat rapidly, but let you keep lean muscle (since they are higher in protein.) The recipes range from pack-and-go food combinations to medium-prep, more creative dishes.

I don't like avocado.

It's very difficult to design a single set plan with meals that please everyone's tastes and cravings every single day. It's much easier to design a delightful variety of recipes you can eat freely, whenever you like, without worrying about macros. You simply pick and choose your favorites.

Can I follow this Fast without eating dairy?

Yes. Substitute coconut cream in place of heavy whipping cream and cheese. Substitute ghee, lard or coconut oil in place of butter. Try using dairy-free mayonnaise instead of cream cheese in the savory recipes.

How much effort do I have to put into this?

Well, you must choose meals and eat them. Beyond that, your recipes do all the work. Depending on the path you choose, you'll eat 4 to 8 recipes each day of your fast.

New Low Carbers:

If you're new to low carb, you can eat more meals each day (if you're hungry) and extend the plan to the full 5 days. Eating more calories helps avoid hunger or tiredness most fat-adapted low carbers don't experience while completing the fast.

Old-School Baconators:

If you're a seasoned low carber, go for it. You can eat fewer meals each day (lowering your daily calories) for increased results. You only have to make it 3 days, and with these recipes, it's beyond easy. If you've been eating ketogenically (very low carb), you can extend the plan to a full week – but no longer. Seriously, 7 days is your maximum.

How do I know I can do this?

The *Almost Zero Fast* is crazy-easy. Everything is written without hard science or complicated math. If you can choose foods you're craving, you can totally do this!

The keto macro guidance you seek is built into every recipe. String your favorites together, and you have a personalized plan that works, without doing any macro-math.

Is the Fat Fast just recipes?

Your fast includes sample menus for 3 days, plus 2 transition days (for a softer transition back to regular low carb). You also have a shopping list for the sample fast, and a printable grid to plan your own meals. Again, these are only suggestions. You are free to choose the meals you want to eat.

You'll get nerdy resources like a list of over 100 foods with almost no carbs, arranged by grocery store section, a one-week Atkins Induction meal plan (for transitioning back), exclusive shortcuts and tips.

Can I exercise during the Fast?

Don't perform heavy exercise while following this plan. Heavy exercise increases hunger and dehydration. Instead, continue being active and include light walking, strength training, or exercises like squats or push-ups. NOTE: exercise is absolutely not necessary during your fast.

FAT FASTING

The *Almost Zero Fat Fast* recipes use high fat foods with (obviously) almost no carbs. Limiting daily calories while eating this way is called "fat fasting." Fat fasting is a well-known technique (backed by authority and medical experts) used to avoid plateau, increase progress, enter deep ketosis quickly or get back on track after a cheat day.

Dr. Robert Atkins

Dr. Atkins was one of the first doctors to recommend his patients try fat fasting: eating a high percentage of daily fat while dropping net carbs and calories.

During a typical fat fast, meals are at least 90% fat. Dr. Atkins recommended eating an 8 oz block of cream cheese slowly during the day. Other versions recommend eating only eggs (the Egg Fast), olive oil, coconut oil, heavy cream and mayonnaise – not very doable or enjoyable.

Jimmy Moore

Jimmy Moore (best-selling author and founder of the website Livin' la Vida Low Carb) explains when fat fasting works best:

"Most people who start livin' la vida low carb and do it by the book have no trouble losing weight, especially if they have a lot to lose. But there is a small percentage of people who, no matter how hard they try to keep their carbs down to 20g, the scale simply refuses to move - even one pound. This can be very frustrating.

If you are in that situation, then I've got some good news for you. There is something you can do as a temporary measure for just a few days to get your body into fat-burning mode: the fat fast! This is an extreme diet plan intended only to get your body to start burning fat and is not meant to be done for more than a few days at the very most. It is ONLY for stalls, plateau, or the most metabolically resistant. Dr. Robert C. Atkins often used this method in his personal practice with patients to help those few people who can't seem to get their low carb lifestyle going because it works extremely well."

Dana Carpender

Dana Carpender (best-selling author and founder of the website Carbsmart) speaks highly of fat fasting, using it in her monthly routine as a low carb reset, to keep her body guessing. Dana describes the purpose of limiting calories, then eating high fat and almost zero carb a few days:

"Fat fasting is a way to overcome metabolic resistance to weight loss or to break a stall. If I don't like what the scale says I'll cut back for a day or two, eating virtually no carbs.

The fat fast catapults you into deep ketosis, with its triple benefit of appetite suppression, metabolic advantage, and protection of muscle mass. Once you're in deep ketosis, calorie restriction forces your body to turn to fat stores for fuel."

The Problem with Most Fat Fasts

Traditional fat fasts are tough to complete, lessening your chance of success. Fasters report feeling hungry and deprived, although they love the rapid fat loss.

Most fat fasts are very low in protein, requiring you to eat very high amounts of fat (90% or higher of total calories). Fat fasts are also notoriously boring. Egg Fast, anyone? Didn't think so.

This Plan Solves Fat Fast Problems

Following the Almost Zero Carb Fat Fast, you'll eat a larger variety of foods more often, keeping you fuller for hours and avoiding the usual hunger issues.

You'll eat more protein and keep more muscle mass while you're on the fast. You'll also eat slightly higher calories (more meals).

This fasting plan is slightly lower in fat, freeing up more calories for protein. You won't be eating sticks of butter, or bar after bar of cream cheese covered in powdered sugar-free Jello (although it's oddly delicious and satisfying).

The Zero Carb Diet

"Zero carb diets" and "no carb diets" are phrases describing extremely low net carb counts. Unless made entirely of butter or oil, no carb meals and recipes are not exactly zero carb. Most have trace amounts of carbs, or less than 1g net carb per serving.

Zero carb meals keep you full and satisfied for at least 6 hours. Some zero carbers eat only once each day, while others eat several times (spread out or all in one sitting.)

Zero carb diets focus on healthy foods from the animal kingdom. These foods are zero carb, or as close as possible. To keep things interesting, some zero carbers use small amounts of veggies for toppings, color, condiments or seasoning.

Zero carbers generally eat:

Protein: bison, beef, pork, chicken, duck, poultry, fish, lamb, goat and eggs

Dairy: unsalted grass-fed butter, cheese and heavy cream

Small amounts of flavorings, such as: garlic, chilies, spices and herbs

The Problem with Zero Carb Diets

Strict zero carb diets are nutritionally solid, but very tough to stick to long-term. There is a serious lack of variety, and monthly food costs run higher than regular low carb or keto diets.

And of course, the oxymoron: If you're eating eggs, cheese and heavy cream, you're not really eating a "zero carb" diet, are you? You're still eating fractions of a gram.

This Plan Avoids Zero Carb Diet Problems

This fasting plan is very close to (but not quite) zero carb, so we can broaden our options immensely. Having more choices besides fatty animal proteins and water greatly increases your chances of completing this plan.

THE ALMOST ZERO CARB FAT FAST

When to Use Your Fast

This plan is for fat-adapted low carbers. Low carbers don't burn carbs (sugars and starches, grains) for energy. Instead, we burn fat stored in the body and the fats we eat. We use the phrase "fat-adapted" to describe this healthier (and more efficient) metabolism.

Use this Fast If:

You're trying to reach ketosis quickly.

You hit a stubborn diet stall or plateau.

You eat a low carb/keto diet, but had a cheat day.

You adjusted your macros, but your scale won't behave.

You need to balance hormones and mood.

If You're Not on a Low Carb or Keto Diet

If you aren't fat-adapted, you'll experience greater hunger and possibly a lack of energy.

If you eat higher amounts of carbs daily and suddenly start this fasting plan, you may develop symptoms of "keto flu."

To avoid keto flu, follow a low carb diet for two weeks (or complete one week of Atkins Induction), then try the Almost Zero Fast if your weight loss stalls.

Heads Up!

Keep in mind this fasting plan is very aggressive. The calories are low, the portions are small (but filling) and the ingredients are strict.

If you have any medical conditions such as diabetes, you must inform your doctor and only follow the fasting plan under medical supervision. As with any dietary change, medication dosages may need adjusting.

Why/How it Works

Your fasting plan blends the best of zero carb diets and fat fasts, achieving excellent results, but in an easier way.

Atkins Fat Fasters report: "If I just had more to eat, and not as much fat, sticking to the program would be easier to do." Many zero carbers point out: "There's not enough variety. I get bored." The Almost Zero Fast solves these issues by using a wider selection of food choices, a little less fat and slightly more calories.

We're keeping the fat a bit lower than the typical 90 to 100% fat fast. We're also adding back more protein (more muscle mass is retained during your fast). We're incorporating more food and recipe options, and finally – we're raising the calories 10 to 15%.

These modifications change the way fat fasting works. The biggest change: This fasting plan is easier to follow and complete. You'll keep more of your heard-earned muscle density, while rapidly losing stored fat.

GETTING STARTED

Days 1 to 5

Follow the plan for 3 to 5 days. Each day, select your favorite recipes, keeping total daily calories around 1200. If you can stick it out past Day 3, an extra day or two almost doubles your fat loss. Yes, doubles your fat loss.

After 3 to 5 days, go back to eating your regular low carb or keto diet. Most people have no trouble going back to their regular plan. Why? Two effects of fat fasting are a decrease in appetite and a disappearance of cravings for sweets: a total win-win situation. There's a high chance you'll eat less after your fast than before your fast, and gain much better portion control.

How to Eat

You'll eat delicious, fat-filled recipes each day, including foods rich in electrolytes (avocados, nuts, mushrooms and dark chocolate).

There is a limit of 1200 total calories per day. Your total doesn't have to be exactly 1200 calories, but it should be close or under. Of course, eating around 1000 calories per day will increase your fat loss, but it's tougher to do.

Most low carbers following this plan eat 5 or 6 small meals per day, each around 200 calories. Others prefer combining recipes, eating 2 or 3 larger meals each day. The choice is entirely up to you.

Recap:

Choose any combination of recipes, eating no more than 1200 total calories each day.

Transitioning Back to Low Carb

After your plan, add an extra meal each day for a few days, increasing your calories and net carbs slightly. This helps ease the transition back to your regular low carb diet with minimal water weight regain.

Many low carbers choose to complete one week of Atkins Induction following the plan. Both methods work extremely well.

Again, this fat fast should only be followed 3 to 5 days. If you use the fast for longer periods of time, there's a risk of entering "starvation mode:" holding on to fat and storing it, losing muscle mass, experiencing nutrient deficiency and slowing your metabolism.

Please don't go there. It's very easy to incorporate this meal plan once or twice a month, or only when needed – safely. For example, you could use this fasting method every other weekend (which is what I personally do.)

Workhorse Recipes

This is where the magic happens. The recipes in your "crazy-easy" fasting plan do all the work. Each recipe has perfectly calculated protein-to-fat ratios, encouraging deep ketosis, and the greatest amount of stored fat loss in the shortest time possible.

Simply choose the recipes you like, without going over your calorie limit. That's it. We've done all the macro-math for you! Every recipe is your personal, fat-burning machine.

Sample menus help you get started quickly. However, the sample menus are only a suggestion. Choose the meals YOU prefer eating during your fast.

The Prep

Most of the recipes are super simple, low or no-prep food combinations. These are easy to make and most travel well outside your home.

Some recipes are so simple, they have only 1 or 2 ingredients. These "recipes" make perfect (fast) low calorie snack options, squashing hunger in seconds.

Some recipes (like the mini meals) are medium-prep. These recipes have more steps involved, but much more flair and creativity. All the recipes in your plan have perfectly calculated macros, so choose the ones you like best.

FAQ

Are the Fast's recipes healthy?

Yes. Your fat fast is filled with the healthiest, inflammation-lowering fats, proteins, fruits and veggies. We've followed low carb and keto diets over 150 years, both for fat loss and health benefits. (Shocked how long low carb's been around and thriving? Me, too.)

Medical professionals use low carb diets to treat diabetes, depression, and many neuro-degenerative diseases like Alzheimer's, rheumatoid arthritis, epilepsy, and (in recent decades) cancerous tumors.

Is this Fasting plan nutritionally sound?

No, not long-term. This fasting plan should only be followed for 3 to 5 days. However, you may fast intermittently each month "to keep your body guessing" or "shake things up."

Will I gain all the weight back?

After completing the Almost Zero Fast, return to your previous way of eating (low carb & keto whole foods, healthy fats). You'll probably gain a fraction of the weight back after the fast, but you'll still keep several pounds off.

Weight gained back isn't necessarily body fat. Weight lost during your plan comes from stored fat, emptying the digestive system and losing excess water – some of which returns when more carbs are added. Transition days prevent or minimize any return of water weight.

What if I'm hungry?

High fat foods are calorie-dense, so your portion sizes are much smaller than typical low carb meals. You may be hungry during the first day or two. If so, try eating every 2 to 3 hours, and choose the highest fat recipes.

Drinking unsweetened tea, coffee or water delays hunger. Fasting for most of the day, then eating a few larger meals later on also helps. Do not add more carbs. If you feel hungry, add an extra recipe to your day.

TIPS

Taking a multivitamin adds vital nutrients not provided during this fasting plan.

Give yourself a day to prepare. Plan a grocery trip and stock up before you start. This seemingly obvious tip prevents going off-plan when there's nothing else in the house to eat. When you start, make snacks right away and store in your fridge/freezer.

Fruit (including tomatoes) and artificial sweeteners can trigger cravings. If you crave, cut these out.

Dana Carpender's Tips:

Every two to three hours, eat about 200 calories.

Eat 1000-1200 calories a day for faster results.

Stay hydrated.

Eat plenty of high quality salt. (pink Himalayan or sea salt)

Don't exceed 3 to 5 days of fat fasting.

Fat fasts are for special occasions or jump-starting your weight loss.

Fat fasting is best for people already on a low carb diet.

Always check with your doctor before beginning, since medication needs may fluctuate.

Reading Food Labels

Many food labels claim their ingredients are "zero carb." Labeling laws allow food companies to print "zero grams of carbs" on the label if the food has less than 1 gram of carbs per serving.

Companies adjust the serving or portion size of the food (lowering the net carbs under 1 gram), so total net carbs can now be listed as "zero" on the label. This action is horribly manipulative and frankly, unacceptable. This alone could sabotage your plan.

Certain sugar substitutes (especially powdered forms), cheese, heavy cream, eggs, deli meats, pepperoni, bacon and spices are common examples of this situation. If you're being extra cautious, count these foods as 0.5g net carbs per serving.

THE PLANNER

Use this planner to map out your 3 to 5 days and track your meals.

Optional transition-back-to-low-carb days are provided. The fields are large and easy to write inside.

Save your completed meal plans for future fasts, marking any days/recipes you really enjoyed or were an easy fit for your lifestyle.

Day 1

Recipe	Calories	Net Carbs
	Totals:	

Day 2

Recipe	Calories	Net Carbs
	Totals:	

Day 3

Recipe	Calories	Net Carbs

Totals:

Day 4

Recipe	Calories	Net Carbs

Totals:

Day 5

Recipe	Calories	Net Carbs

Totals:

TRANSITION DAYS

After 3 to 5 days of the Almost Zero plan, your goal is preventing water weight from returning (due to a sudden increase in carbs.)

Transition days bridge the gap between almost zero carb and regular low carb. Keep eating the recipes from your plan, but add 1 or 2 extra recipes per day, increasing your calories slightly each day. This, in turn, increases your net carbs only slightly – preventing most of the water weight from suddenly returning.

Another option is following an Atkins Induction meal plan for a week (or two) after your fat fast, instead of adding transition days.

Transition Day 1 (optional)

Recipe	Calories	Net Carbs

Totals:

Transition Day 2 (optional)

Recipe	Calories	Net Carbs

Totals:

SAMPLE 3-DAY PLAN WITH 2 TRANSITION DAYS

The first day in this sample plan starts out with very low net carbs. Let's rip the Band-Aid right off. Day 2 is higher in fat and calories, helping reduce hunger.

TIP: *Eat a meal/recipe every three hours during the day. Eating calories more evenly throughout your day keeps energy levels high and staves off hunger. Drink plenty of water or decaf coffee/tea.*

Day 1

4.g total net carbs for the day.

Coffee/Tea with Butter & Cream
Bacon & Eggs
Egg Salad

Mustard Bacon Wraps
Chicken & Ranch or Blue Cheese
Vanilla Cinnamon Mascarpone

1252 Calories; 112g Fat (80.5% calories from fat); 55g Protein; 6g Carbohydrate; 2g Dietary Fiber.

Day 2

3.4g total net carbs for the day.

Coffee/Tea with Butter & Cream
Bacon & Eggs
Lemon Cheesecake Bites

Zero Tuna Salad
Creamy Buttered Spinach
Garlic Chicken

1288 Calories; 116g Fat (81% calories from fat); 63g Protein; 7.4g Carbohydrate; 4g Dietary Fiber.

Day 3 has more snacks. Day 3 is when you may experience cravings. If you stay busy, it's easier to dodge the sugary urges and complete the plan.

TIP: *Heading out for adventure or errands? Choose grab-and-go recipes that travel well for your mid-day meals. Staying busy at home? You'll have ready-made meals at your fingertips. There's no need to linger in your kitchen.*

Day 3

6.4g total net carbs for the day.

Bacon, Chives & Cheddar
Deli Meat & Cheese Roll-Ups
Simple Side Salad

Buttered Beef
Mushroom Sauté
Vanilla Chocolate Mousse

1275 Calories; 117g Fat (82.5% calories from fat); 78g Protein; 10.4g Carbohydrate; 4g Dietary Fiber.

Days 4 and 5 are your optional, "transition-back-to-low-carb" days. Transition days are slightly higher in net carbs and calories, preventing sudden return of water weight.

To create a transition day, simply add an extra recipe or two. For example, drink butter coffee, eat an extra snack, enjoy a double serving at dinner or indulge in dessert.

Day 4 (transition day)

6.5g total net carbs for the day.

Cream & Eggs   Hot Cheese Crackers
Pepperoni Chips & Dip   Buttered Roasted Broccoli
Zero Chicken Salad   Blackberry Cream Cheese

> 1236 Calories; 113g Fat (82.2% calories from fat); 92g Protein; 10.3g Carbohydrate; 3.8g Dietary Fiber.

Day 5 (transition day)

7.85g total net carbs for the day.

Mustard Bacon Wraps   Mini Burger
Macadamia Nuts   Soda Float
Cucumbers, Celery & Ranch   Hot Cheese Crackers

> 1433 Calories; 140g Fat (84.4% calories from fat); 48g Protein; 11g Carbohydrate; 3.15g Dietary Fiber.

SHOPPING LIST

This shopping list is for the sample 5-day plan. Each day of the sample plan has different recipes, so this list has quite a few items.

Fortunately, any leftover items are the lowest net carb keto foods (and great to have around.) The recipes in your fasting plan use common low carb ingredients. If you choose to follow your plan with a week of Atkins Induction, you'll use ALL remaining items.

Repeating recipes during your plan significantly reduces your shopping list.

This is easily accomplished by making several servings of a dessert or chicken/tuna/egg salads. You may also choose to eat fewer meals during the day by fasting or doubling up on portions.

The meals are very small, but calorie-dense. If you're prone to frequent hunger, eating every 2 to 3 hours during the day helps tremendously. Of course, drinking plenty of water helps, too. Black coffee and plain tea also stave off hunger, but concentrate on decaffeinated options.

Eggs & Dairy

butter, 8 oz
heavy cream, 8 oz
sour cream, 2 tbsp
Neufchatel cheese, 8 oz
cheddar cheese, 11 oz
jalapeño cheese, 8 oz
Parmesan cheese, 3 tbsp
mascarpone, 4 oz
eggs, 7 whole + 1 yolk

Meat & Seafood

tuna, 2 oz (sub chicken)
chicken, 10 oz
sausage link/patty, 2 oz (sub ground beef)
ham/deli meat, 1 oz (sub chicken)
bacon, 10 slices
ground beef, 4 oz
pepperoni slices, 5 thick or 10 thin or 1/2 oz

Condiments

Ranch, 1/3 cup (sub blue cheese)
mayo, 1/4 cup (sub any healthy fat)
mustard, 1 tsp

Fruit & Veggies

garlic, 2 cloves
lemon juice, 1 tsp
lettuce leaves, 9 leaves
spinach, 10 oz
cucumber slices, 1/2 cup
celery, 2 stalks
dill pickle, 1 spear
tomato, 1 small
mushrooms, 1/2 cup
broccoli, 1/2 cup
blackberries, 10 berries

Seasoning

garlic powder, to taste
Italian seasoning, to taste
stevia, to taste
salt and pepper, to taste
cocoa powder, 2 tbsp
cinnamon, to taste
vanilla extract, to taste

Drinks

coffee
flavored sparkling water
diet soda (optional; limit or
avoid artificial sweeteners)

Fats

coconut oil, 1 1/2 tbsp (sub olive oil/butter)
macadamia nuts, 20 whole nuts

BREAKFAST
Bacon and Cheese Waffles (pg 29)
with egg and asparagus

ASPARAGUS OMELET

1g net carb per serving - 255 calories
Servings: 2

INGREDIENTS

2 bacon slices, cooked

1 tbsp coconut oil (or MCT oil)

1 oz chopped asparagus

1 tbsp heavy cream

2 eggs

1 tsp flax seeds, ground

1 oz cheddar cheese, shredded

METHOD

Cook the bacon, remove and set aside. Chop when cooled. Add 1 tablespoon coconut or MCT oil to the skillet and mix with the bacon drippings.

Combine the chopped bacon, chopped asparagus, heavy cream, eggs and ground flax seeds into a bowl and stir well.

When the skillet is hot, pour in the contents of the bowl. Flip the omelet once, then add the cheddar cheese. Fold the omelet over in half. Continue cooking 1 to 2 more minutes. Plate and serve.

Per Serving: 255 Calories; 22g Fat (78.5% calories from fat); 12g Protein; 2g Carbohydrate; 0.8g Dietary Fiber.

BACON & CREAM CHEESE

2g net carbs per serving - 204 calories
Servings: 1

INGREDIENTS

3 bacon slices, cooked

1 oz Neufchatel cheese

favorite herbs and spices,

or extract for sweet versions

METHOD

Easy: Spread plain or flavored cream cheese on slices of cooked bacon.

Try savory versions with garlic, chives, onion powder or rosemary.

For sweet versions, add vanilla, almond or maple extract, and stevia to taste. You may spread a very small amount of sugar-free jam on top, but adding very sweet-tasting foods may cause cravings.

Per Serving: 204 Calories; 18g Fat (80.6% calories from fat); 16g Protein; 2g Carbohydrate; trace Dietary Fiber.

BACON & EGGS

2g net carbs per serving - 221 calories
Servings: 1

INGREDIENTS

2 whole eggs, cooked any way

2 bacon slices (sub sausage)

salt and pepper, to taste

METHOD

Cook bacon in a small skillet. Halfway through cooking, add the egg. When both are finished cooking, plate (with grease too!) and eat.

Per Serving: 221 Calories; 16g Fat (66.4% calories from fat); 16g Protein; 2g Carbohydrate; 0g Dietary Fiber.

BACON & CHEESE WAFFLES

1.8g net carbs per serving - 212 calories
Servings: 6

INGREDIENTS

batter from Classic Crepes recipe

4 oz sharp cheddar cheese, shredded

4 bacon slices, cooked and chopped

1 drop liquid stevia

6 tbsp sour cream

METHOD

Preheat the waffle iron. Precook bacon and prepare Classic Crepe batter according to recipe.

Add 1 drop liquid stevia and chopped bacon to the batter.

Pour batter into the waffle iron, then sprinkle shredded cheddar on top.

Cook 2 to 5 minutes until waffles lift out easily with a fork.

Top with butter, sour cream, a poached egg (add the calories), or cinnamon and stevia.

TIP: *Heat 5 crushed raspberries, stevia and butter over medium heat, stirring until a thick syrup forms (a minute or two). Instant keto syrup!*

Per Serving: 212 Calories; 15g Fat (64.1% calories from fat); 23g Protein; 2g Carbohydrate; trace Dietary Fiber.

BACON, CHIVES & CHEDDAR

2g net carbs per serving - 204 calories
Servings: 1

INGREDIENTS

3 bacon slices, cooked

1 oz sharp cheddar cheese

chives, chopped fine

favorite herbs and spices, to taste

salt and pepper, to taste

METHOD

Sprinkle shredded cheddar cheese, chives and seasoning over slices of cooked bacon.

Bake or broil a few minutes until cheese melts.

Use a parchment paper-lined or greased baking sheet to prevent sticking.

Per Serving: 204 Calories; 12g Fat (53.8% calories from fat); 32g Protein; 2g Carbohydrate; 0g Dietary Fiber.

BREAKFAST CASSEROLE

0.7g net carbs per serving - 285 calories
Servings: 12

INGREDIENTS

12 oz sausage, ground

8 whole eggs

1/2 c heavy cream

1/2 c broccoli florets, chopped

1 tsp sea salt

1 tsp black pepper

6 oz sharp cheddar cheese, grated

METHOD

Preheat oven to 350 F.

Brown the sausage in a skillet, let cool, then place in an oven-safe dish (Include the grease!).

In a bowl, whisk together eggs, heavy cream, broccoli, sea salt and pepper. Pour the egg mixture over the sausage, and add a layer of cheese on top.

Optional: Sprinkle with minced peppers. These add color without adding too many carbs.

Tent with foil and bake for 15 minutes. Uncover and bake until casserole is golden brown and bubbly, about 15 to 20 more minutes.

Per Serving: 285 Calories; 23g Fat (70.9% calories from fat); 23g Protein; 1g Carbohydrate; 0.3g Dietary Fiber.

Breakfast Casserole

BREAKFAST PIZZA

2g net carbs per serving (1 pizza) - 285 calories
Servings: 3 mini pizzas

INGREDIENTS

1/2 batter from Oopsie Roll/
Flatbread recipe

1 tbsp butter, melted

1 c spinach leaves (sub any dark
greens)

1/2 avocado, pitted and sliced

4 green bell pepper rings

2 oz feta cheese, crumbled

2 whole eggs

METHOD

Preheat your oven to 325 F.

Prepare and cook 3 flatbread pieces using the Marvelous Oopsie recipe (pg 81).

Brush melted butter over the flatbread.

Pile pepper slices (optional), avocado, feta, and spinach or dark greens on top.

Crack an egg over the toppings.

Bake until egg is fully cooked, the flatbread browns and cheese is melted.

Per Serving: 285 Calories; 23g Fat (73.5% calories from fat); 14g Protein; 5g Carbohydrate; 3g Dietary Fiber.

Breakfast Pizza

BREAKFAST SAUSAGE BALLS

0.5g net carbs per serving (4 balls) • 237 calories
Servings: 8

INGREDIENTS

1/2 lb sausage, ground

4 oz ground beef

3 whole eggs

4 oz sharp cheddar cheese, shredded

2 tbsp red onion, finely chopped

1/2 tsp black pepper

METHOD

Preheat oven to 350 F. Place all ingredients in a bowl and mix thoroughly using your hands.

Roll handfuls of the mixture into 1 1/2 inch balls (or drop by the spoonful) and place on a baking sheet. Leave room between each ball.

Bake 17 to 22 minutes.

Stores well in a sealed container in the fridge (or freezer.) Makes about 32 sausage balls.

Per Serving: 237 Calories; 18g Fat (68.7% calories from fat); 18g Protein; 1g Carbohydrate; 0.5g Dietary Fiber.

CLASSIC CREPES

0.5g net carbs per serving (1 crepe) - 104 calories
Servings: 6

INGREDIENTS

2 whole eggs

3 oz Neufchatel cheese, softened

1/4 tsp vanilla extract

1/2 tsp ground cinnamon

dash sea salt

liquid stevia, to taste

2 tbsp unsalted butter

METHOD

Combine cream cheese, eggs, vanilla, cinnamon, sea salt and stevia (optional) in a mixing bowl.

Blend well until very smooth using a whisk, hand mixer or blender. Let the crepe batter rest for 2 to 3 minutes.

Add butter to a skillet over medium heat. Gently pour the batter into circles.

Cook crepes 3 to 4 minutes, or until undersides are golden brown.

Loosen the crepe edges with a spatula, flip the crepe over, then cook another minute or two.

Slide crepes out of the skillet and store in a warm oven until ready to eat (180 to 200 F). You may also place the warm crepes on paper towels to cool, then store in the fridge (lasts a few days) or freezer (lasts a month).

Add butter to the skillet and repeat the steps with remaining batter.

Top with more butter or whipped heavy cream.

Per Serving: 104 Calories; 10g Fat (83.5% calories from fat); 7g Protein; 0.5g Carbohydrate; trace Dietary Fiber.

Classic Egg Crepes

CLASSIC EGG CREPES

1g net carb per serving - 206 calories
Servings: 4

INGREDIENTS

1/2 batter from Classic Crepes
recipe
4 bacon slices
4 whole eggs
1 tbsp unsalted butter
1 tsp parsley, chopped
1/4 tsp sea salt
1/4 tsp black pepper

METHOD

Prepare the Classic Crepes recipe batter (pg 39).
Set aside half in the fridge (keeps several days).

Heat a 12-inch nonstick skillet over medium heat. Add
some of the batter and swirl to completely cover skillet.

Cook until underside of crepe starts to brown, about 2
minutes. Loosen the edge of crepe with a spatula, lift
up and flip. Cook another 1 to 2 minutes, then slide out
of skillet onto a paper towel to cool. Repeat until all 4
crepes are done.

Preheat oven to 350 F. Place crepes on a baking sheet.
Put 2 half strips of bacon in the center of each crepe,
then carefully crack an egg over the top.

Fold the edges of each crepe toward the center. Use the
egg whites as glue.

Season with sea salt and pepper, then bake until egg
whites set, about 9 to 11 minutes.

Remove from oven, garnish with chopped parsley and
serve immediately.

Per Serving: 206 Calories; 17g Fat (76.6% calories from fat); 11g Protein; 1g Carbohydrate; trace Dietary Fiber.

Cream Cheese Pancakes

CREAM & EGGS

1g net carb per serving - 183 calories
Servings: 1

INGREDIENTS

1 whole egg

1 egg yolk

1 tbsp heavy cream

salt and pepper, to taste

favorite herbs and spices, to taste

METHOD

Prepare as scrambled eggs with your favorite herbs and spices, or use chopped hard-boiled eggs and mix into a mock egg salad.

TIP: Add 1 tablespoon of minced celery or serve wrapped in lettuce leaves for added crunch.

183 Calories; 15g Fat (76.7% calories from fat); 9g Protein; 1g Carbohydrate; 0g Dietary Fiber.

CREAM CHEESE PANCAKES

1.8g net carbs per serving - 221 calories
Servings: 2

INGREDIENTS

2 whole eggs

2 oz Neufchatel cheese, softened

1/2 tsp cinnamon, ground

stevia, to taste, optional

1 tbsp butter

METHOD

Blend eggs, cream cheese, cinnamon and stevia until smooth. Let the batter sit until the bubbles settle (about 2 minutes).

Add butter to a large skillet over medium heat. Pour small circles of the batter into the skillet.

Cook until golden brown (about 2 minutes).

Per Serving: 221 Calories; 20g Fat (81.2% calories from fat); 17g Protein; 2g Carbohydrate; 0.2 Dietary Fiber.

CREAMY HOT SAUSAGE

1g net carb per serving - 213 calories
Servings: 1

INGREDIENTS

1 oz sausage, crumbled or sliced
(ground, link, patty)
1 oz Neufchatel cheese, softened
1/2 tsp hot mustard
(sub yellow mustard)
salt, to taste

METHOD

Crumble and cook the sausage, then place into a bowl with softened cream cheese, hot mustard and salt.

Add any sausage grease left over from cooking.

Mix well.

Per Serving: 213 Calories; 20g Fat (84.8% calories from fat); 14g Protein; 1g Carbohydrate; trace Dietary Fiber.

CRUNCHY CEREAL

2g net carbs per serving - 225 calories
Servings: 1

INGREDIENTS

2 tbsp pecans, ground
2 tbsp shredded coconut meat, unsweetened
2 tbsp heavy cream
pinch of salt
stevia, to taste (optional)

METHOD

This recipe works well hot or cold. Mix all ingredients together and eat immediately, or heat on medium in a microwave for 1 minute before serving.

The cold version of this recipe is much better when using more heavy cream. If you choose to add more, don't forget to add the calories and carbs.

Per Serving: 225 Calories; 22g Fat (89.5% calories from fat); 1g Protein; 4g Carbohydrate; 2g Dietary Fiber.

FLAVORED BACON

2g net carbs per serving - 225 calories
Servings: 1

INGREDIENTS

4 bacon slices, cooked

METHOD

Sprinkle bacon slices with salt and pepper, spices or herbs. (Brushing with yellow mustard or sugar-free maple syrup is also delicious.)

Cook bacon slices as desired.

TIP: *Make sure to eat as much of the grease as possible. This is easily accomplished by cooking an egg or cream cheese pancake with the bacon.*

Per Serving: 225 Calories; 22g Fat (89.5% calories from fat); 1g Protein; 4g Carbohydrate; 2g Dietary Fiber.

SAUSAGE & CHEDDAR

1g net carb per serving - 231 calories
Servings: 1

INGREDIENTS

1 sausage link (or patty)
1 oz cheddar cheese

METHOD

Place cheese on top of sausage and eat. This is much more exciting with a specialty cheese, and works hot or cold.

Get creative, stay simple or just use what's in the fridge.

Per Serving: 231 Calories; 21g Fat (80.9% calories from fat); 10g Protein; 1g Carbohydrate; 0g Dietary Fiber.

Spinach Feta Crepes

SPINACH FETA CREPES

1g net carb per serving - 234 calories
Servings: 6

INGREDIENTS

1/2 batter from Classic Crepes
recipe
2 tsp olive oil
1 clove garlic
1/4 tsp sea salt
1/2 tsp black pepper
1/2 tsp red pepper flakes
10 oz spinach leaf, whole
6 oz Parmesan cheese, grated
3 oz feta cheese

METHOD

Prepare the Classic Crepes batter (pg 39).

Heat a 12-inch non-stick skillet over medium heat.

Add 1/4 of the crepe batter and swirl to completely cover skillet. Cook until the underside of crepe starts to brown, or about 2 minutes.

Loosen the edge of crepe with spatula, lift it up and flip. Cook another 1 to 2 minutes, then slide out of skillet onto a paper towel or cutting board to cool. Repeat with remaining batter.

Add olive oil and garlic to a large skillet over medium heat. Add sea salt, black pepper and red pepper flakes. Cook 2 minutes.

Stir in spinach and continue cooking another 5 to 6 minutes, or until spinach wilts.

Reduce to low heat, stir in Parmesan and feta cheese, then turn off the heat. Let sit 1 minute before removing from skillet. Wipe the skillet clean and heat again on medium low.

Place one crepe flat in the skillet, then drop 1 ounce of feta cheese in the center of the crepe. Layer the spinach-cheese mixture on top.

Fold the crepe in half, then fold it over again to make a triangle. Cook 2 to 3 minutes, flip and cook another 2 to 3 minutes or until cheese is fully melted. Repeat with remaining crepes.

Per Serving: 234 Calories; 18g Fat (69.5% calories from fat); 16g Protein; 1g Carbohydrate; trace Dietary Fiber.

BUTTER COCONUT COFFEE

0.8g net carbs per serving - 191 calories
Servings: 1

INGREDIENTS

12 oz coffee, strong, freshly brewed

2 tbsp heavy cream

2 tsp coconut oil (sub grass-fed
butter)

1/4 tsp vanilla extract (sub sugar-free
vanilla syrup), optional

liquid stevia, to taste, optional

METHOD

Add all ingredients to your blender and mix until frothy.
An inexpensive mini frother or hand-held blender works
well for mixing.

Frozen version: Pour into ice cube trays and freeze.

Pop out and store frozen in a container. Toss six cubes
into a blender or food processor, and blend until
smooth and icy.

Per Serving: 191 Calories; 20g Fat (95.8% calories from fat); 1g Protein;
0.8g Carbohydrate; 0g Dietary Fiber.

DRINKS

Butter Coconut Coffee

COFFEE/TEA WITH BUTTER & CREAM

0.8g net carbs per serving - 208 calories
Servings: 1

INGREDIENTS

12 oz coffee, brewed (or tea)

2 tbsp heavy cream (or coconut oil)

1 tbsp butter

METHOD

Add all ingredients to your blender and mix until frothy. An inexpensive mini frother or hand-held blender works well for mixing.

Frozen version: Pour into ice cube trays and freeze.

Pop out and store frozen in a container. Toss six cubes into a blender or food processor, and blend until smooth and icy.

Per Serving: 208 Calories; 22g Fat (97.5% calories from fat); trace Protein; 0.8g Carbohydrate; 0g Dietary Fiber.

FLAVORED SPARKLING SELTZER

0g net carbs per serving - 0 calories
Servings: 1

INGREDIENTS

16 oz seltzer water

natural flavor of choice

METHOD

To a tall glass of seltzer water, add a splash of lemon or lime, some orange zest, or a few frozen berries like raspberries, blueberries or blackberries.

Add 5 to 10 calories and 0.5g net carbs to your macros if using berries.

Per Serving: 0 Calories; 0g Fat (0.0% calories from fat); 0g Protein; 0g Carbohydrate; 0g Dietary Fiber.

Flavored Sparkling Seltzer

SODA FLOAT

1.6g net carbs per serving - 205 calories
Servings: 1

INGREDIENTS

4 tbsp heavy cream

12 oz diet soda (or flavored water of choice)

METHOD

Whip heavy cream until soft peaks form.

Spoon into a frosty mug, then pour ice-cold soda or flavored sparkling water over the whipped cream.

Per Serving: 205 Calories; 22g Fat (94.8% calories from fat); 1g Protein; 1.6g Carbohydrate; 0g Dietary Fiber.

VANILLA COCONUT ICY CREAM

2g net carbs per serving - 203 calories
Servings: 1

INGREDIENTS

1/3 c coconut cream, unsweetened

1/2 c filtered water

1/4 tsp vanilla extract

5 ice cubes

liquid stevia (optional) to taste

METHOD

Pour coconut cream, water, vanilla and stevia in a blender.

Begin blending, adding one ice cube at a time.

Blend just until ice cubes are crushed.

Pour into a glass and drink immediately.

Per Serving: 203 Calories; 21g Fat (91.9% calories from fat); 3g Protein; 3g Carbohydrate; 1g Dietary Fiber.

SAUCES &
SPREADS

Citrus Avocado Butter (pg 51)

ALMOND CREAM CHEESE

2g net carbs per serving - 193 calories
Servings: 1

INGREDIENTS

1 tbsp almond butter

1 oz Neufchatel cheese

favorite herbs and spices, to taste

stevia, optional for sweet versions

METHOD

Mix with your favorite sweet flavors: cinnamon, nutmeg, vanilla, maple extract, unsweetened shredded coconut, or cocoa. Or savory flavors: salt and pepper, lemon, chili powder, garlic, espresso or bacon.

TIP: *Drop dots (teaspoonfuls) on parchment paper and freeze for instant fat bombs. Store in an airtight container in the freezer until ready to eat.*

Per Serving: 193 Calories; 17g Fat (81.2% calories from fat); 14g Protein; 4g Carbohydrate; 2g Dietary Fiber.

AVOCADO BACON MASH

2g net carbs per serving - 235 calories
Servings: 1

INGREDIENTS

1/2 avocado, pitted and cubed

2 bacon slices, cooked and crumbled

salt and pepper, to taste

METHOD

Remove avocado pit and meat from skin.

Mash avocado meat, add crumbled bacon, salt, pepper and seasoning to taste, then mix well.

Per Serving: 235 Calories; 20g Fat (76.0% calories from fat); 6g Protein; 10g Carbohydrate; 8g Dietary Fiber.

CHOCOLATE SAUCE

1g net carb per serving (2 tbsp) — 14 calories
Servings: 8

INGREDIENTS

1 cup water

8 tbsp cocoa powder

2 tbsp liquid stevia (or equiv)

1/8 teaspoon salt

1 tbsp vanilla extract

METHOD

Mix water, cocoa powder, sweetener and salt in a pot. Bring sauce to a boil, then reduce heat.

Simmer on low heat 5 to 8 minutes, or until sauce thickens.

Remove from heat. Stir in vanilla.

Total Recipe: 111 Calories; 6g Fat (28.8% calories from fat); 8g Protein; 24g Carbohydrate; 14g Dietary Fiber.
Per Serving: 14 Calories; 1g Fat (28.8% calories from fat); 1g Protein; 3g Carbohydrate; 2g Dietary Fiber.

CITRUS AVOCADO BUTTER

0.5g Net carbs per serving - 105 calories
Servings: 4

INGREDIENTS

6 oz avocado, mashed

1 tsp lemon or lime juice (sub zest)

4 tbsp unsalted butter, softened

1 clove garlic, minced fine

1 tbsp cilantro, chopped

2 tbsp cumin, ground

1/8 tsp sea salt

1/8 tsp black pepper

METHOD

Peel and pit the avocados, then mash.

Place all ingredients into a food processor and pulse until well combined.

Refrigerate in a sealed container 3 to 4 hours.

Before serving, whip with a fork.

Spread over veggies, seafood, beef or poultry.

TIP: *Choose Haas avocados. They are higher in fiber and lower in net carbs.*

Per Serving: 105 Calories; 12g Fat (98.7% calories from fat); trace Protein; 1g Carbohydrate; 0.5g Dietary Fiber.

CREAMY COCONUT BUTTER

1g net carb per serving (2 tbsp) - 266 calories
Servings: 8

INGREDIENTS

4 c unsweetened coconut meat

1/2 tsp coconut oil

METHOD

Place coconut meat into your food processor, and process for ten minutes.

Scrape the sides of the food processor bowl with a rubber spatula, then continue blending well.

Process again for another five to seven minutes, or until slightly fluid.

Scrape your coconut butter into a jar or container with a lid. Store in the pantry or fridge.

Per Serving: 266 Calories; 25g Fat (84.8% calories from fat); 3g Protein; 8g Carbohydrate; 7g Dietary Fiber.

FLAVORED CREAM CHEESE

1.4g net carbs per serving - 198 calories
Servings: 1

INGREDIENTS

2 oz cream cheese

flavor of choice

METHOD

Cream cheese is very versatile, grabbing almost any flavor.

Try cinnamon, cocoa powder, vanilla or lemon extracts with a little liquid stevia for a sweet taste.

Add fresh herbs and spices, diced green onion, chili peppers or bacon for a savory taste.

Per Serving: 198 Calories; 20g Fat (89.9% calories from fat); 4g Protein; 1.4g Carbohydrate; trace Dietary Fiber.

MACADAMIA CREAM CHEESE

2g net carbs per serving - 194 calories
Servings: 1

INGREDIENTS

1/2 oz macadamia nuts, crushed
(about 10 nuts)
1 oz Neufchatel cheese
favorite herbs, spices or extract

METHOD

Crush macadamia nuts (sub 1/2 ounce macadamia nut butter) and mix with your favorite flavors.

Sweet versions: Use cinnamon, nutmeg, vanilla, maple extract, unsweetened shredded coconut, cocoa or espresso.

Savory versions: Use lemon pepper, chili powder, garlic or bacon.

Eat raw, or slather on celery sticks, lettuce leaves, a cucumber/dill pickle spear (add 3 calories and 0.3g net carbs per spear), or zucchini slices (add 2 calories and 0.2g net carbs per slice).

Per Serving: 194 Calories; 18g Fat (84.7% calories from fat); 12g Protein; 3g Carbohydrate; 1g Dietary Fiber.

SPICY KETO MAYONNAISE

0g net carbs per serving (1 tbsp) **-** 128 calories
Servings: 16

INGREDIENTS

1 c extra virgin olive oil

2 egg yolks

1 tbsp wine vinegar

1 tbsp lemon juice

1 tsp dry mustard

1/4 tsp sea salt

dash Tabasco (or other

zero carb hot sauce)

METHOD

Pour olive oil into a measuring cup with a spout and set aside.

Place the rest of the ingredients in a jar with a lid. Immerse a stick blender into the mixture and blend for several seconds, or until uniformly smooth.

Keep the blender running and (very slowly) pour in the olive oil.

Work the blender up and down in the jar, mixing thoroughly.

Stop when the mayonnaise stiffens and oil puddles on the surface. Cover and store in the fridge.

Per Serving: 128 Calories; 14g Fat (98.2% calories from fat); trace Protein; 0g Carbohydrate; 0g Dietary Fiber.

SALADS

CHICKEN AVOCADO SALAD

1g net carb per serving - 278 calories
Servings: 2

INGREDIENTS

1/4 lg avocado, peeled and pitted

2 tbsp ranch salad dressing (or blue cheese dressing)

2 tsp extra virgin olive oil (or coconut / MCT oil)

1 oz provolone cheese

4 oz chicken, cooked and chopped

2 c lettuce, your choice

1 c spinach leaf

1 slice red onion (optional)

METHOD

Chop the avocado, provolone cheese and chicken.

Mix 2 tablespoons of ranch dressing with 2 teaspoons of olive oil, coconut oil or MCT oil, and blend well.

Combine all ingredients in a bowl and serve on a pile of fresh lettuce and spinach leaves.

Garnish with a few (thin) slices of red onion, and speckles of tomato or red sweet peppers.

Go easy on the garnish. Go for color, not carbs!

Per Serving: 278 Calories; 27g Fat (79.8% calories from fat); 12g Protein; 3g Carbohydrate; 2g Dietary Fiber.

CHICKEN BROCCOLI SALAD

2g net carbs per serving - 194 calories
Servings: 1

INGREDIENTS

1/2 c broccoli florets

1 oz Neufchatel cheese, softened

1 tbsp celery, diced fine

dash onion powder

salt and pepper, to taste

2 oz chicken, cooked

METHOD

Chop the broccoli, then mix in cream cheese until thoroughly coated.

Add celery, onion powder, salt and pepper.

Add the chicken, toss and serve.

194 Calories; 11g Fat (88.8% calories from fat); 2g Protein; 3g Carbohydrate; 1g Dietary Fiber.

CHICKEN SALAD

1g net carb per serving - 219 calories
Servings: 1

INGREDIENTS

2 c romaine lettuce, chopped (sub spinach, 1/2 cup cucumber slices)

2 oz chicken, chopped or shredded

2 tbsp celery, diced small

2 tbsp ranch salad dressing (sub blue cheese or 1 tbsp of olive oil/ Mayo)

salt and pepper, to taste

METHOD

This simple chicken salad has the satisfying crunch you're craving.

Chop and mix together any way you prefer.

Per Serving: 219 Calories; 23g Fat (74.1% calories from fat); 10g Protein; 3g Carbohydrate; 2g Dietary Fiber.

EGG SALAD

2g net carbs per serving - 194 calories
Servings: 1

INGREDIENTS

2 c romaine lettuce, chopped
(sub spinach, arugula or 1/2 cup
cucumber slices)
1 whole egg, hard-boiled,
chopped or shredded
2 tbsp celery, diced small
1 tbsp mayonnaise (sub olive oil,
or 2 tbsp of ranch/blue cheese
dressing)
dash mustard (powdered or
yellow; not spicy or Dijon)
salt and pepper, to taste

METHOD

This salad is easy to prepare and store ahead
of time.

You may use any sugar-free, zero carb salad
dressing.

Add extra dressing or oil to increase the fat
percentage (and the calories.)

TIP: *Make single-serving salads in a small cup or mug.*

Per Serving: 278 Calories; 25g Fat (79.8% calories from fat); 12g Protein; 3g Carbohydrate; 2g Dietary Fiber.

FRENCH SPINACH SALAD

2g net carbs per serving - 209 calories
Servings: 1

INGREDIENTS

2 c fresh spinach

4 tsp extra virgin olive oil

3 tsp cider vinegar

1/2 tsp sugar-free ketchup

(sub 1/4 tsp tomato paste)

1 med mushroom, sliced

1 slice bacon, cooked

METHOD

Wash spinach leaves and place in a bowl.

Whisk together olive oil, vinegar and sugar-free ketchup.

Pour dressing over the spinach and toss well.

Top your salad with mushroom slices and crumbled bacon.

TIP: *Add a diced, hard-boiled egg for more protein and healthy fat. Add 70 calories and 0.7g net carbs to your macros.*

Per Serving: 209 Calories; 21g Fat (89.3% calories from fat); 4g Protein; 4g Carbohydrate; 2g Dietary Fiber.

SIMPLE SIDE SALAD

2g net carbs per serving - 195 calories
Servings: 1

INGREDIENTS

1/2 c spinach

1/2 c arugula

1 radish, sliced

1 tbsp red pepper, minced

3 cucumber slices, diced

1/4 c cauliflower, chopped florets

1 1/2 tbsp extra virgin olive oil

1 tsp red wine vinegar

METHOD

You're well-versed in salad making. Go for it. Reach for the stars.

Other Leafy Greens (net carbs in 1/2 cup):

Arugula, Mustard Greens, Parsley (Chopped), Spinach 0.1g

Bok Choy, Endive, Iceberg, Romaine, Alfalfa Sprouts 0.2g

Add-In Veggies (net carbs in 1/4 cup):

Broccoli Florets 0.38g
Cauliflower 0.45g
Cucumber 0.5g
Mushroom 0.65g
Squash 0.65g
Zucchini 0.75g
Bell Pepper (1 tbsp) 0.2g
Tomato (1/4" slice) 0.4g
Tomato (1 cherry) 0.5g

Base salad (no add-ins)
Per Serving: 195 Calories; 20g Fat (90.5% calories from fat); 1g Protein; 4g Carbohydrate; 2g Dietary Fiber.

TOMATO FETA SALAD

2g net carbs per serving - 228 calories
Servings: 1

INGREDIENTS

1/4 c tomato, diced

1 oz feta cheese, crumbled

1 tbsp olive oil

5 olives, sliced or chopped

salt and pepper, to taste

basil and oregano, to taste

METHOD

Mix all ingredients together in a small bowl.

TIP: *Be careful with this recipe. After eating very low carb, tomatoes have enough natural sugar to cause cravings.*

Per Serving: 194 Calories; 17g Fat (76.6% calories from fat); 19g Protein; 3g Carbohydrate; 1g Dietary Fiber.

ZERO CHICKEN SALAD

0g net carbs per serving - 192 calories
Servings: 1

INGREDIENTS

1/4 c chicken, cooked and chopped

1 tbsp mayonnaise

mustard (a tiny amount), to taste

salt and pepper, to taste

romaine lettuce leaves

METHOD

Mix all ingredients together and serve over lettuce, or roll up in lettuce leaves, forming a wrap.

Per Serving: 192 Calories; 18g Fat (83.9% calories from fat); 8g Protein; trace Carbohydrate; 0g Dietary Fiber.

ZERO TUNA SALAD

0g net carbs per serving - 185 calories
Servings: 1

INGREDIENTS

1/4 c tuna

1 tbsp mayonnaise

mustard (a tiny amount), to taste

salt and pepper, to taste

romaine lettuce leaves

METHOD

Mix all ingredients together and serve over lettuce, or roll up in lettuce leaves, forming a wrap.

Per Serving: 185 Calories; 15g Fat (69.6% calories from fat); 14g Protein; 0g Carbohydrate; 0g Dietary Fiber.

SNACKS

Buttered Salmon (pg 68)
with egg, cream sauce
and cherry tomato

ALMONDS

2g net carbs per serving - 167 calories
Servings: 1

INGREDIENTS

1 oz almonds (about 20-25 nuts)

favorite herbs or spices, to taste

METHOD

Eat raw or roasted.

Coat in melted butter, olive oil or coconut oil, then sprinkle your favorite seasonings over the top.

Roast at 325 F until browned.

Per Serving: 167 Calories; 14g Fat (75.4% calories from fat); 6g Protein; 5g Carbohydrate; 3g Dietary Fiber.

BACON STUFFED EGGS

1g net carb per serving (2 halves) - 204 calories
Servings: 6

INGREDIENTS

6 whole eggs, hardboiled

3 bacon slices, cooked and crumbled

1/2 avocado (ripened

4 tbsp mayonnaise

1 oz sharp cheddar cheese, shredded

sea salt, to taste

black pepper, to taste

METHOD

Hardboil the eggs and cook the bacon.

Scoop out the inside of an avocado half and mash using a fork.

Peel the boiled eggs and cut in half, lengthwise.

Scoop out yolks and place into a bowl. Mash the yolks with a fork until finely crumbled. Add avocado, mayonnaise, cheddar cheese, crumbled bacon, salt and pepper to taste. Mix well.

Using a spoon, scoop up the yolk mixture and fill in the egg cavities. Sprinkle with paprika, then store in the fridge until ready to serve.

Per Serving: 204 Calories; 17g Fat (74.7% calories from fat); 12g Protein; 2g Carbohydrate; 1g Dietary Fiber.

BACON WRAPPED ASPARAGUS

2g net carbs per serving (4 wrapped spears) - 106 calories
Servings: 6

INGREDIENTS

24 asparagus spears, washed
and trimmed

12 bacon slices

1 tbsp extra virgin olive oil

1 tsp garlic powder

sea salt, to taste

black pepper, to taste

METHOD

Preheat your oven to 400 F.

Place a greased wire baking rack on top of a cookie sheet.

Drizzle olive oil over the asparagus. Sprinkle with garlic powder, salt and black pepper to taste.

Cut bacon slices lengthwise, forming narrow strips.

Wrap each strip tightly around an asparagus stalk.

You may also bundle several spears together and wrap with a whole bacon strip.

Place wrapped asparagus (seam side down) on a wire baking rack, over a baking sheet or sheet of foil to catch the grease.

Bake 8 to 10 minutes. Turn over and bake another 10 to 15 minutes, or until bacon is almost crispy.

Place under the broiler for 1 to 2 minutes for crispier bacon.

Per Serving: 106 Calories; 8g Fat (68.0% calories from fat); 5g Protein; 4g Carbohydrate; 2g Dietary Fiber.

BEEF & SOUR CREAM

1g net carb per serving - 231 calories
Servings: 1

INGREDIENTS

2 oz ground beef

2 tbsp sour cream

favorite herbs and spices, to taste

salt and pepper, to taste

METHOD

Brown your beef for best taste. Add sour cream and seasoning of choice.

Try Mexican spices, ground mustard, red pepper flakes, garlic, onion powder or chili to vary the taste.

Per Serving: 231 Calories; 21g Fat (80.8% calories from fat); 10g Protein; 1g Carbohydrate; 0g Dietary Fiber.

BRUSSELS SPROUTS & BACON

2g net carbs per serving - 208 calories
Servings: 1

INGREDIENTS

1/2 c Brussels sprouts

1 bacon slice, cooked and chopped

1 1/2 tbsp butter (sub olive oil)

lemon juice, splash

salt and pepper, to taste

METHOD

Cold version: Shred or chop sprouts, and spritz with lemon. Add chopped bacon, salt, pepper and olive oil. Toss well and plate.

Hot version: Cook sprouts with butter (or olive oil) and chopped raw bacon slice. Remove from heat, add salt and pepper, then spritz with lemon. Toss well and serve.

TIP: *Top with a layer of grated Parmesan or Asiago cheese, and brown in the oven until bubbly.*

Per Serving: 208 Calories; 20g Fat (85.3% calories from fat); 4g Protein; 4g Carbohydrate; 2g Dietary Fiber.

BUFFALO CHICKEN & CELERY

0g net carbs per serving - 196 calories
Servings: 1

INGREDIENTS

2 oz chicken, cooked

1 tbsp butter

dash hot sauce

salt, to taste

garlic powder, to taste

1 stalk celery

METHOD

Sauté chicken in butter and hot sauce.

Add salt and garlic powder to taste.

Serve inside a piece of celery.

You may drizzle a small amount of blue cheese or ranch dressing on top.

Per Serving: 208 Calories; 20g Fat (85.3% calories from fat); 4g Protein; 4g Carbohydrate; 2g Dietary Fiber.

BUTTERED BEEF

0g net carbs per serving - 227 calories
Servings: 1

INGREDIENTS

2 oz ground beef

1/2 tbsp butter

favorite herbs and spices, to taste

salt and pepper, to taste

METHOD

This is as simple as it gets. Brown beef for best taste.

Add butter, and spices or herbs. Use mustard, red pepper flakes, garlic, onion powder or chili to vary the taste.

Per Serving: 227 Calories; 21g Fat (83.1% calories from fat); 9g Protein; 0g Carbohydrate; 0g Dietary Fiber.

BUTTERED SALMON

0g net carbs per serving - 234 calories
Servings: 1

INGREDIENTS

4 oz smoked salmon

olive oil (sub coconut oil)

1 tbsp butter

capers (optional)

salt and pepper, to taste

METHOD

Coat salmon filet with olive oil or coconut oil.

Bake or pan-fry in butter, adding salt and pepper.

Toss in the capers (optional) and glaze the pan by adding a splash of lemon juice or white wine.

Serve immediately, or flake and store in the fridge (excellent for making creamy salmon salad).

Per Serving: 234 Calories; 16g Fat (63.9% calories from fat); 21g Protein; trace Carbohydrate; 0g Dietary Fiber.

CHICKEN CORDON BLEU ROLL-UPS

1g net carb per serving - 239 calories
Servings: 1

INGREDIENTS

2 oz ham (2 thick slices)

1 oz Swiss cheese (2 thin slices)

3 oz chicken (3 thick slices)

METHOD

Lay ham slices flat and place Swiss on top.

Drop a pile of the chicken on top of the cheese, near the edge.

Roll up like a jelly roll and fasten the bundle with a toothpick.

Place bundles in a baking dish and bake at 350 F for 10 to 15 minutes, or until cheese is melted and meats are hot. (You may also use a microwave.)

Per Serving: 239 Calories; 17g Fat (66.6% calories from fat); 19g Protein; 1g Carbohydrate; 0g Dietary Fiber.

CHICKEN & RANCH OR BLUE CHEESE

0g net carbs per serving - 230 calories
Servings: 1

INGREDIENTS

3 oz chicken breast, cooked

2 tbsp ranch salad dressing (sub

blue cheese)

salt and pepper, to taste

METHOD

Cook the chicken any way you prefer. (Strips are an easy dipping shape.)

Using a stove-top skillet method produces a nice, crispy brown crust on the chicken, enhancing your flavor considerably.

Cooking with butter increases the healthy fat (and the calories.) Dip hot or cold chicken into full-fat ranch or blue cheese salad dressing.

TIP: *Add a splash of hot sauce to the chicken or dressing and include a few celery pieces on the side.*
Per Serving: 230 Calories; 19g Fat (76.2% calories from fat); 16g Protein; 0g Carbohydrate; 0g Dietary Fiber.

Coconut Flour Bread

COCONUT FLOUR BREAD

1g net carb per slice - 266 calories
Servings: 12

INGREDIENTS

4 oz unsalted butter, room temp

5 lg whole eggs

1/2 tsp apple cider vinegar

1/2 c coconut flour

1 tsp baking powder

1/2 tsp baking soda

1/2 tsp sea salt

METHOD

A firm, dense bread with minimal rise.

Preheat your oven to 350 F.

Using a mixer, cream butter until smooth.

In another bowl, mix together eggs and vinegar. Add the egg mixture to the mixer. Blend well.

In a large bowl, whisk the dry ingredients together (coconut flour, baking powder, baking soda and salt). Turn on the mixer and slowly add spoonfuls of the dry ingredients until well blended.

Butter a bread pan, muffin tins or deep baking dish. Add the batter and place into the oven.

Bake 20 minutes, then check every few minutes to see if the bread is completely baked (a knife or toothpick comes out clean).

Depending on the size of the loaf pan or dish, bake times may vary.

If bread browns too quickly, tent with foil. Remove from oven and allow to cool before slicing.

TIP: *Use this recipe for muffins, crusts, crackers (add salt, pepper, spices, herbs or grated cheese) and cookies (add liquid stevia, cocoa, shaved dark chocolate, nuts or unsweetened coconut shreds).*

Per Serving: 266 Calories; 23g Fat (78.4% calories from fat); 4g Protein; 4g Carbohydrate; 3g Dietary Fiber.

CREAMY CHIVE CHICKEN

0.5g net carbs per serving - 194 calories
Servings: 1

INGREDIENTS

3 oz chicken

1 tsp butter

salt and pepper, to taste

1 tbsp sour cream (full fat)

chives, chopped fine

METHOD

Bake or pan-fry chicken in butter, salt and pepper.

You may glaze the pan with a splash of lemon juice or white wine.

Mix the sour cream with chopped chives and spread over cooked chicken.

TIP: *This recipe makes a great cold salad.*

Per Serving: 194 Calories; 16g Fat (76.1% calories from fat); 11g Protein; 0.5g Carbohydrate; 0g Dietary Fiber.

CRISPY PARM CHIPS

1g net carb per serving (6 chips) - 132 calories
Servings: 3

INGREDIENTS

1 c cauliflower, grated

1 tsp parsley, chopped

1/2 tsp rosemary, chopped

1 c Parmesan cheese, grated

1 clove garlic, pressed

onion powder

sea salt, to taste

black pepper, to taste

METHOD

Preheat your oven to 400 F.

Grate the cauliflower into a bowl or use riced cauliflower.

Chop the parsley and rosemary. Add both to the cauliflower rice. Toss well, then mix in Parmesan cheese, garlic, onion powder, salt and pepper.

Form 18-ish loose balls with the mixture (about 1 inch in diameter) and place them on a parchment paper-lined baking tray.

Using the bottom of a drinking glass, press each ball flat.

Bake 5 minutes, turn each circle over, then bake another 5 minutes or until golden brown.

Remove from the oven and allow to cool for a few minutes until crispy.

TIPS: *Top chips with shredded/sliced meats, chicken/egg/tuna salads or dip into your favorite creamy sauce. Drape larger circles over a cool knife and hold steady until firm (about 30 seconds to a minute) for crispy, cheesy taco shells.*

You may also sink the warm circles into greased muffin tins and let cool, creating small, crunchy cheese cups when hard.

Per Serving: 132 Calories; 8g Fat (57.2% calories from fat); 12g Protein; 2g Carbohydrate; 1g Dietary Fiber.

CRUNCHY CHICKEN TENDERS

0.25g net carbs per serving - 228 calories
Servings: 12

INGREDIENTS

2 lbs chicken breast

1 whole egg

4 oz sharp cheddar cheese, grated

8 oz Parmesan cheese, grated

1/2 tsp sea salt

1/2 tsp black pepper

1/2 tsp basil, finely chopped

METHOD

Preheat oven to 375 F.

Cut the chicken into strips.

Scramble the egg and place into a bowl.

Mix the cheddar and Parmesan together in a separate bowl.

Dip each strip into the egg, then roll through the cheddar Parmesan mix, fully coating both sides.

Place dipped and rolled chicken strips on a greased baking sheet, leaving space between each piece.

Sprinkle with sea salt, black pepper and basil.

Bake 15 to 20 minutes until golden brown and crispy.

TIPS: *Meet your macros by dipping in a healthy, high-fat sauce.*

Remember to add the extra calories to your daily total. Remember to add the calories and net carbs from any add-ins to your macros.

Per Serving: 228 Calories; 13g Fat (52.0% calories from fat); 30g Protein; 0.25g Carbohydrate; trace Dietary Fiber.

DELI MEAT & CHEESE ROLL-UPS

1.4g net carbs per serving - 193 calories
Servings: 1

INGREDIENTS

1 oz ham (about 2 slices),

(sub any other meat)

1 1/2 oz Neufchatel cheese

salt and pepper, to taste

favorite herbs and spices, to taste

METHOD

Spread cream cheese on a slice of ham (or turkey, chicken, roast beef).

Add fresh herbs, spices, salt and pepper, minced garlic or onion to the cream cheese for flavor.

Sprinkle seasonings over the top, and roll up.

Variations: Try ham and Swiss, roast beef and cheddar, turkey and mozzarella, or chicken and hot pepper cheese.

TIPS: *Stack a few lettuce leaves, and a THIN slice of tomato or onion between the meat and cheese for color, and crunch.*

You may also dice the deli meat and mix it into the cream cheese.

Substitute 1 ounce (1 slice) of cheddar (or other cheese) for the cream cheese.

Per Serving: 193 Calories; 17g Fat (80.0% calories from fat); 21g Protein; 1.4g Carbohydrate; trace Dietary Fiber.

DELI BACON WRAPS

1.3g net carbs per serving - 216 calories
Servings: 1

INGREDIENTS

2 bacon slices, cooked

1 oz chicken (about 2 slices),

cooked

1 tbsp mayonnaise (sub olive oil)

salt and pepper, to taste

favorite herbs and spices, to taste

METHOD

Place bacon on a slice of deli meat (turkey, chicken or roast beef) coated with mayo.

Sprinkle seasonings over the top and roll up.

TIP: Add fat to your macros by dipping in ranch, zero carb Italian or blue cheese dressing. Remember to add the extra calories to your daily total.

Per Serving: 216 Calories; 21g Fat (84.8% calories from fat); 8g Protein; 1.3g Carbohydrate; 0g Dietary Fiber.

GARLIC CHICKEN

0.2g net carbs per serving - 231 calories
Servings: 1

INGREDIENTS

3 oz chicken

1 tbsp butter

garlic, 1 pressed clove

salt and pepper, to taste

METHOD

Bake or pan-fry chicken with garlic, butter, salt and pepper until lightly browned.

You may glaze the pan with a splash of lemon juice, apple cider/balsamic vinegar or white wine.

TIP: *Add 1 tbsp heavy cream, mustard, red pepper flakes, garlic, onion powder or chili to vary the taste. Add 60 calories and 0.4g net carbs to your macros when adding cream.*

Per Serving: 231 Calories; 21g Fat (81.5% calories from fat); 11g Protein; 0.2 Carbohydrate; 0g Dietary Fiber.

HOT CHEESE CRACKERS

1g net carb per serving - 213 calories
Servings: 8

INGREDIENTS

1 c sharp cheddar cheese,
shredded

1 c hot pepper cheese, shredded

1 tsp garlic powder

1 tsp salt, to taste

METHOD

Line a plate with greased parchment paper.

Sprinkle cheese into 8 small, circular piles 2 inches in diameter and about 1/4 inch high. Leave space between each cheese circle.

Sprinkle with garlic and salt (or any herb/spice).

Microwave on high 60 to 90 seconds until cheese bubbles and edges turn golden brown.

Let cool in the microwave 30 to 60 seconds.

Remove and gently peel the circles off the parchment paper, then set aside on paper towels to harden.

TIP: *Experiment with different blends of cheese and add extras like fresh cilantro, ground spices, minced onion or crumbled cooked bacon.*

Per Serving: 213 Calories; 18g Fat (76% calories from fat); 35g Protein; 1g Carbohydrate; 0g Dietary Fiber.

LEMON SPINACH RICOTTA CREPES

2g net carbs per serving - 189 calories
Servings: 6

INGREDIENTS

10 oz ricotta cheese

2 tsp lemon zest, finely grated

garlic powder, to taste

2 tbsp red pepper, finely chopped

1/4 tsp sea salt

1/4 tsp black pepper

6 crepes from Classic Crepes recipe

12 oz chopped spinach

METHOD

In a medium bowl, stir together ricotta cheese, lemon zest, garlic, red peppers, salt and black pepper.

Place a crepe on a flat surface and cover with a layer of ricotta cheese filling, about 1/4 inch thick. Make sure the layer of ricotta cheese covers the entire edge of the crepe. This acts like glue to keep your roll tight.

Spread a layer of spinach on top of the cheese.

Starting with the edge closest to you, roll the crepe up tightly, making sure the closing edge is sealed.

Place the rolled crepe seam side down on a plate.

Repeat with remaining crepes and filling.

Cover and refrigerate for at least two hours, or overnight. Serve chilled.

TIP: *Roll chilled crepes in finely grated cheese before slicing.*

Per Serving: 189 Calories; 15g Fat (70.6% calories from fat); 10g Protein; 4g Carbohydrate; 2g Dietary Fiber.

MACADAMIA NUTS

1.5g net carbs per serving - 204 calories
Servings: 1

INGREDIENTS

1 oz macadamia nuts (10-12 nuts)

favorite herbs and spices, to taste

METHOD

Add the macadamia nuts to a skillet over medium heat.

Add salt and toss until golden brown.

Oven method:

Add a small amount of butter, olive oil or coconut oil, then sprinkle your favorite seasonings over the top.

Roast in the oven at 325 F or in a skillet over medium heat until browned.

Per Serving: 204 Calories; 20g Fat (88.2% calories from fat); 2g Protein; 3.9g Carbohydrate; 2.4g Dietary Fiber.

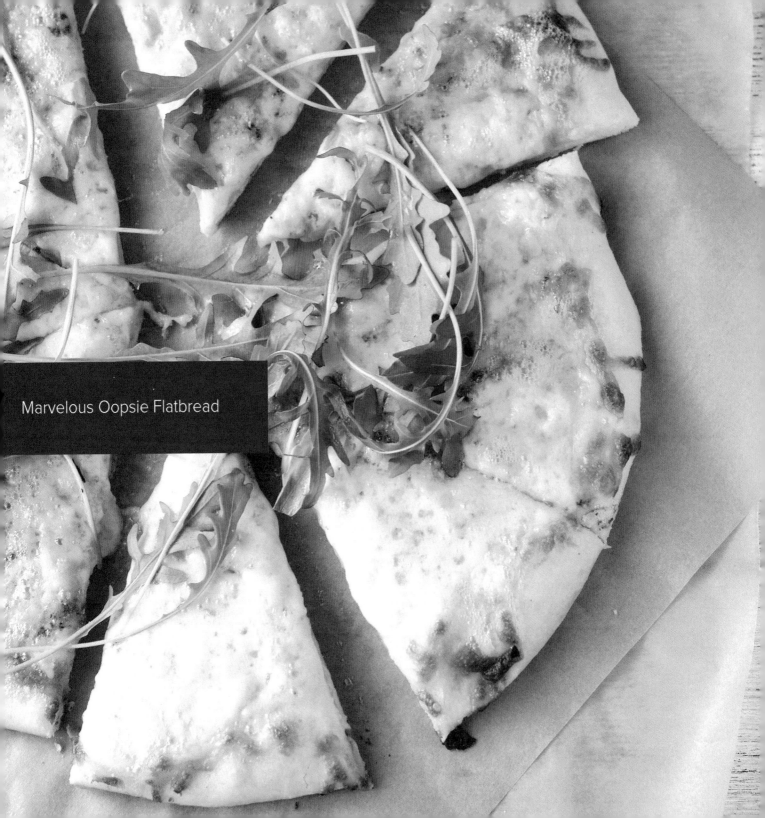

Marvelous Oopsie Flatbread

MARVELOUS OOPSIE ROLLS/FLATBREAD

1g net carb per serving (1 roll) - 127 calories
Servings: 4

INGREDIENTS

3 whole eggs

1/2 tsp baking powder

1 drop liquid stevia (optional)

3 oz Neufchatel cheese

1/2 tsp psyllium husk

dash sea salt

Savory versions: Use a sprinkle of Parmesan cheese, chia seeds, spices or herbs.

Sweet versions: Add a sprinkle of cocoa powder, cinnamon or unsweetened shredded coconut.

METHOD

Preheat oven to 300 F. Separate the eggs into yolks and whites.

Add the egg whites and baking powder to a mixing bowl, beating until stiff peaks form.

In a separate bowl, mix together yolks, liquid stevia, cream cheese, psyllium husk and sea salt.

Using a spatula, gently fold the yolk mixture into the white mixture, just until blended. Do not over mix!

Marvelous Oopsie Rolls: Drop 4 mounds of batter onto a greased baking sheet and flatten slightly using the back of a spoon.

Marvelous Oopsie Flatbread: Drop 2 large mounds onto a greased baking sheet and gently spread out into larger, flatter circles.

Bake 5 to 10 minutes. Remove from oven and allow to cool a few minutes. Carefully move the finished rolls/flatbread to a cooling rack.

Garnish rolls while still warm.

Top flatbread with cheese, herbs, spices, veggies or cooked meat. Place back into the oven and bake until toppings are brown.

Per Serving: 127 Calories; 11g Fat (78.4% calories from fat); 13g Protein; 1g Carbohydrate; trace Dietary Fiber.

MINI BURGER

2g net carbs per serving - 224 calories
Servings: 1

INGREDIENTS

2 romaine lettuce leaves

1 tsp mustard

smear of mayonnaise

2 oz ground beef, cooked

1 dill pickle spear (sub 1 thin slice
of tomato)

1 bacon slice, cooked

salt and pepper, to taste

METHOD

Slather lettuce leaves with mustard and mayo.

Pile ground beef and bacon on the lettuce.

Top with salt and pepper (or your favorite seasoning).

Serve with a pickle spear or slices on the side.

TIP: Serve it on Oopsie Rolls/Flatbread and
add 1-2g net carbs.

Per Serving: 224 Calories; 18g Fat (74.0% calories from fat); 12g Protein; 3g Carbohydrate; 1g Dietary Fiber.

MUSTARD BACON WRAPS

1g net carb per serving - 121 calories
Servings: 1 (2 wraps)

INGREDIENTS

2 bacon slices, cooked

1 oz chicken (2 thin deli slices)

1 tsp mustard, yellow or hot

salt and pepper, to taste

favorite herbs and spices, to taste

METHOD

Place bacon on a slice of mustard-coated deli meat
(sub turkey, chicken, roast beef or ham).

Sprinkle seasonings over the top, and roll up.

TIP: These make excellent 60-calorie, half-carb
snacks that pack and travel well outside your home.

Per Serving: 121 Calories; 10g Fat (70.8% calories from fat); 8g Protein; 1g Carbohydrate; trace Dietary Fiber.

ORANGE PECAN SANDWICHES

1g net carb per serving (2 pecan sandwiches) - 184 calories
Servings: 1

INGREDIENTS

4 pecan halves

1/2 tbsp unsalted butter

1 oz Neufchatel cheese

1/2 tsp orange zest

pinch sea salt

METHOD

Toast the pecans at 350 F in the oven for 8 to 10 minutes, set aside and allow to cool.

Soften the butter and cream cheese, add the orange zest and mix well until smooth and creamy.

Spread the butter-orange mixture between two pecan halves, sprinkle with sea salt and enjoy.

TIP: Use other citrus zests, cinnamon and stevia, chives, onion or garlic powder, flavored extracts, cocoa, grated dark chocolate or espresso.

Per Serving: 184 Calories; 17g Fat (85.6% calories from fat); 11g Protein; 2g Carbohydrate; 1g Dietary Fiber.

PECANS

2g net carbs per serving - 100 calories
Servings: 1

INGREDIENTS

1 oz pecan halves (about 20 halves)

favorite herbs or spices, to taste

METHOD

Eat raw or roasted. Coat in melted butter, olive oil or coconut oil, then sprinkle your favorite seasonings over the top.

Roast in the oven at 325 F or in a skillet over medium heat.

TIPS: *Add 100 calories to the recipe by adding 1 tbsp melted butter. Add 100 calories and 0.7g net carbs to the recipe by adding 1 ounce of Neufchatel cheese to cold versions.*

Per Serving: 100 Calories; 10g Fat (85.4% calories from fat); 1g Protein; 3g Carbohydrate; 1g Dietary Fiber.

PEPPERONI & RANCH

1.1g net carbs per serving - 208 calories
Servings: 1

INGREDIENTS

1 oz pepperoni (about 14 slices)

ranch salad dressing (for light

dipping only)

METHOD

Dip pepperoni chips in a small amount of ranch dressing.

TIP: *For incredible crunch, place chips flat on a baking sheet, sprinkle with Parmesan cheese and bake until golden brown and crispy.*

Per Serving: 208 Calories; 19g Fat (79.8% calories from fat); 9g Protein; 1.1g Carbohydrate; trace Dietary Fiber.

PEPPERONI CHIPS & DIP

1.8g net carbs per serving - 229 calories
Servings: 1

INGREDIENTS

1 oz pepperoni (about 14 slices)

1 oz Neufchatel cheese, whipped

(sub 2 tbsp ranch or blue cheese)

favorite herbs and spices, to taste

salt and pepper, to taste

METHOD

Place pepperoni slices on a plate and microwave 60 to 90 seconds, or until crisp. You may also bake them on a baking sheet or foil in the oven for a few minutes.

Mix spices or herbs, salt and pepper into the cream cheese.

Spread the cream cheese on each pepperoni chip, or dip the chips into ranch/blue cheese salad dressing.

Per Serving: 229 Calories; 19g Fat (82.1% calories from fat); 17g Protein; 2.3g Carbohydrate; 0.5g Dietary Fiber.

JUST
VEGGIES

ASPARAGUS & LEMON MAYO

1g net carb per serving - 212 calories
Servings: 1

INGREDIENTS

5 asparagus spears, cooked or
raw

2 tbsp mayonnaise (sub butter)

spritz of lemon juice (sub zest)

salt and pepper, to taste

METHOD

Beyond easy: Dip spears in flavored mayonnaise.

Use a spicy mayonnaise version for more kick.

Per Serving: 212 Calories; 22g Fat (91.2% calories from fat); 2g Protein; 3g Carbohydrate; 2g Dietary Fiber.

AVOCADO CITRUS HALF

2g net carbs per serving - 202 calories
Servings: 1

INGREDIENTS

1/2 avocado

1 tsp olive oil

splash of lime or lemon juice
(sub zest)

salt and pepper, to taste

METHOD

Remove avocado meat from the skin.

Mash, add olive oil, lime/lemon juice or zest,
salt, pepper and any other favorite seasoning.

Per Serving: 202 Calories; 18g Fat (81.0% calories from fat); 2g Protein; 9g Carbohydrate; 7g Dietary Fiber.

BUTTERED ASPARAGUS

1g net carb per serving - 112 calories
Servings: 1

INGREDIENTS

3 oz asparagus

1 tbsp butter (sub coconut oil or MCT oil)

salt and pepper, to taste

METHOD

Roast asparagus in butter and salt for best taste (or brown in a skillet, stove top.)

TIPS: *Subbing bacon grease for butter adds incredible flavor!*

Top with slivered roasted almonds when you're craving crunch.

Per Serving: 112 Calories; 11g Fat (89.2% calories from fat); 1g Protein; 2g Carbohydrate; 1g Dietary Fiber.

BUTTERED ROASTED BROCCOLI

1g net carb per serving - 214 calories
Servings: 1

INGREDIENTS

1/2 c fresh broccoli florets

2 tbsp butter

salt and pepper, to taste

METHOD

Chop broccoli and roast, cook, steam or leave raw.

Place into a bowl.

Melt butter over low heat, adding salt and pepper to taste.

Remove from heat and pour over broccoli.

Per Serving: 214 Calories; 22g Fat (94.2% calories from fat); 1g Protein; 2g Carbohydrate; 1g Dietary Fiber.

CAULIFLOWER & RANCH

2g net carbs per serving - 194 calories
Servings: 1

INGREDIENTS

1 c cauliflower florets, chopped

3 tbsp ranch salad dressing

METHOD

Dip florets in ranch or any high fat spread.

Or, rice the florets, add the ranch (plus a little grated cheese) and bake until golden brown.

You may sub blue cheese dressing (or any other zero carb/sugar-free dressing) for the ranch.

Per Serving: 194 Calories; 18g Fat (85.3% calories from fat); 4g Protein; 5g Carbohydrate; 3g Dietary Fiber.

CAULI RICE

2g net carbs per serving - 227 calories
Servings: 1

INGREDIENTS

1 c cauliflower, riced or finely chopped

2 tbsp heavy cream

1 tbsp butter

salt and pepper, to taste

METHOD

Mix all ingredients together and cook on the stove top, or bake until golden brown and bubbly.

Crunchy version: Sprinkle grated Parmesan cheese over the top.

Per Serving: 227 Calories; 22g Fat (86.6% calories from fat); 3g Protein; 5g Carbohydrate; 3g Dietary Fiber.

Cauli Rice

CELERY RIBS & CREAM CHEESE

2g net carbs per serving - 195 calories
Servings: 1

INGREDIENTS

2 oz Neufchatel cheese

1 lg celery rib, cut into pieces

salt and pepper, to taste

favorite herbs and spices, to taste

METHOD

Blend cream cheese, salt and pepper in a small bowl.

Cut celery rib into bite-size pieces and fill with cream cheese mixture.

Per Serving: 195 Calories; 18g Fat (82.2% calories from fat); 22g Protein; 3g Carbohydrate; 1g Dietary Fiber.

CREAMY BUTTERED SPINACH

1g net carb per serving - 233 calories
Servings: 2

INGREDIENTS

10 oz fresh (or frozen) spinach, chopped

3 tbsp butter

2 tbsp Neufchatel cheese, softened

salt and pepper, to taste

METHOD

Cook spinach stove-top or in the microwave.

Press firmly though a strainer or blot, removing excess water.

Transfer spinach to a bowl, then stir in butter and cream cheese until completely melted. Salt and pepper (or spice/herb) to taste.

Per Serving: 233 Calories; 21g Fat (82.1% calories from fat); 10g Protein; 5g Carbohydrate; 4g Dietary Fiber.

CUCUMBERS, CELERY & RANCH

1g net carb per serving - 197 calories
Servings: 1

INGREDIENTS

1/2 c cucumber slices

2 stalk celery

3 tbsp ranch salad dressing

METHOD

This simple salad has more fiber and crunch (with the added celery), and is easy to prep and store ahead of time.

Slice or dice all ingredients and mix well.
You may sub blue cheese or any other sugar-free, zero carb salad dressing.

TIP: *Make several servings at once, then store individual portions in a small cups or mugs.*

Per Serving: 197 Calories; 19g Fat (85.8% calories from fat); 4g Protein; 5g Carbohydrate; 4g Dietary Fiber.

CUCUMBERS & SOUR CREAM DIP

2g net carbs per serving - 117 calories
Servings: 1

INGREDIENTS

2 oz sour cream

1/4 c cucumber slices

salt and pepper, to taste

favorite herbs and spices, to taste

METHOD

Slice cucumber and set aside.

Add salt, pepper, and spices or herbs to the sour cream.

Mix well, then add cucumber.

Eat immediately, or chill for an hour/overnight.

Per Serving: 117 Calories; 11g Fat (83.6% calories from fat); 2g Protein; 3g Carbohydrate; 1g Dietary Fiber.

DILL PICKLES & CREAM CHEESE

1.4g net carb per serving - 100 calories
Servings: 1

INGREDIENTS

1 dill pickle spear

1 oz Neufchatel cheese

salt and pepper, to taste

METHOD

Spread the cream cheese on the pickle spear. Be sure to check the jar for net carbs.

You may wrap the pickle in a thin slice of deli meat (add 30-ish calories and 0.25g net carbs).

TIP: *Low carbers rave about the craving relief dill pickles provide. If you're adventurous, they rave about drinking the pickle juice, too.*

Per Serving: 100 Calories; 9g Fat (81.6% calories from fat); 11g Protein; 1.4g Carbohydrate; trace Dietary Fiber.

ITALIAN ZUCCHINI

2g net carbs per serving - 194 calories
Servings: 1

INGREDIENTS

1/2 c zucchini slices

1 1/2 tbsp olive oil

1 tsp red wine vinegar

salt and pepper, to taste favorite

herbs and spices, to taste

METHOD

This recipe works hot or cold.

Coat the zucchini slices with olive oil, vinegar, herbs/spices, salt and pepper (or marinate overnight.)

Optional: Top with 1 oz of feta cheese.
(Add 1g net carb to your macros.)

Serve cold or roast in the oven until golden brown.

TIP: *Add a light sprinkle of Parmesan cheese or dry Italian salad dressing mix, a splash of lemon, or infused olive oil to boost your flavor.*

Per Serving: 196 Calories; 20g Fat (90.7% calories from fat); 1g Protein; 3g Carbohydrate; 1g Dietary Fiber.

Italian Zucchini

MARINATED OLIVES

2g net carbs per serving - 181 calories
Servings: 1

INGREDIENTS

20 whole olives

2 tsp olive oil

splash of red wine vinegar

salt and pepper, to taste

favorite spices and herbs, to taste

METHOD

Mix all ingredients together in a small bowl or container. Marinate the olive mixture at least an hour, but preferably overnight.

These are great hot or cold, especially when paired with diced Italian cheeses.

TIPS: *Green olives are generally lower in net carbs than Greek olives. Olives packed in olive oil are fine to use, as long as net carbs are low. Be sure to check your labels.*

Per Serving: 181 Calories; 18g Fat (87.2% calories from fat); 1g Protein; 5g Carbohydrate; 3g Dietary Fiber.

MUSHROOM SAUTÉ

1g net carb per serving - 205 calories
Servings: 1

INGREDIENTS

1/2 c mushrooms, sliced

1 tbsp butter

1 oz Neufchatel cheese (or Boursin brand cheese)

favorite herbs and spices, to taste

METHOD

Sauté mushrooms in a skillet on the stove top with butter, cream cheese (or other soft cheese), herbs/spices, salt and pepper.

Or, bake your shrooms in a small oven-proof dish until brown and bubbly.

TIP: Add a light sprinkle of Parmesan cheese or dry Italian salad dressing mix, a splash of lemon, or infused olive oil to boost your flavor.

Per Serving: 205 Calories; 20g Fat (85.7% calories from fat); 12g Protein; 2g Carbohydrate; 1g Dietary Fiber.

MINI MEALS
Bold Salmon Skewers (pg 98)
with zucchini

ADOBO CRUSTED TILAPIA

0.7g net carbs per serving - 289 calories
Servings: 1

INGREDIENTS

16 oz tilapia, fillets

4 tbsp extra virgin olive oil

2 tbsp Adobo spice mix (store-bought or DIY in directions)

2 tsp lime juice

4 tbsp Parmesan cheese, grated

1/2 tsp sea salt

1/2 tsp black pepper

METHOD

Preheat an oven safe skillet to medium high.

Add olive oil, coating the bottom well.

Rinse tilapia in cold water and pat dry.

Coat both sides of the fish with Adobo spice mix.

DIY Adobo Spice: Mix equal amounts of onion powder, garlic powder, turmeric, oregano, cumin, sea salt and black pepper.

Place fillets in the skillet. Cook 6 minutes on each side, adding lime juice just after flipping.

Sprinkle grated Parmesan cheese, sea salt and black pepper over the fillets.

Place the skillet in your oven and broil a few minutes, or until crispy.

Remove from the oven and allow to cool slightly before serving.

Per Serving: 289 Calories; 18g Fat (56.0% calories from fat); 32g Protein; 0.7g Carbohydrate; trace Dietary Fiber.

BACON CRUSTED CHICKEN

0.6g net carbs per serving - 248 calories
Servings: 5

INGREDIENTS

1 lb chicken breast (whole, strips or chunks)

1/4 c mayonnaise

6 strips bacon, cooked and crumbled

2 cloves garlic, minced

1/4 tsp sea salt, or to taste

METHOD

Preheat your oven to 450 F.

Line a baking sheet or pan with foil, and grease lightly.

Mix crumbled bacon, garlic and sea salt together until pieces are very fine.

Place the bacon mixture in a large bowl or shallow pan.

Add mayonnaise to a medium bowl. Dip chicken breasts or pieces into the mayo until lightly coated, then roll through the bacon pieces, coating all sides thoroughly.

Place rolled and coated chicken on a baking sheet.

Repeat the process with remaining chicken.

Bake 15 to 20 minutes at 450 F, until chicken is fully cooked and bacon is crisp.

Optional: *Dip in mustard, ranch or blue cheese dressing, sugar-free barbecue sauce/ ketchup or hot sauce. (Remember to add the calories and net carbs from the sauce to your macros.)*

Per Serving: 248 Calories; 20g Fat (71.7% calories from fat); 18g Protein; 0.6g Carbohydrate; 0g Dietary Fiber.

BOLD SALMON SKEWERS

0.5g net carbs per serving - 295 calories
Servings: 4

INGREDIENTS

12 oz salmon, fillets

1 clove garlic, minced

3 tbsp parsley, chopped fine

1/3 c olive oil

1 tbsp red wine vinegar

1/4 tsp sea salt

1/4 tsp red pepper

1/2 bell pepper

METHOD

Preheat grill or oven 450 to 550 F.

Cut salmon into 1 1/2 inch pieces.

Mince the garlic and chop the parsley. Set some parsley aside for a garnish.

Mix olive oil, vinegar, garlic, parsley, sea salt and pepper in a bowl and set aside.

Cut veggies into 1 to 2 inch squares and place on skewers with salmon cubes.

Brush the kebabs with olive oil, thoroughly coating both sides.

Sprinkle with more parsley, salt and pepper.

Bake, broil or grill, turning once until fish is cooked (about 4 to 6 minutes).

When kebabs are cooked, arrange on a plate, sprinkle with crumbled bacon and spoon the vinaigrette over the top.

TIP: *Enhance your vinaigrette by adding the leftover bacon grease.*

Per Serving: 295 Calories; 24g Fat (73.6% calories from fat); 19g Protein; 0.5g Carbohydrate; 0g Dietary Fiber.

BROCCOLI CHEESE SOUP

1.6g net carbs per serving - 244 calories
Servings: 5

INGREDIENTS

1 1/2 c broccoli florets, steamed

4 oz cream cheese, softened

2 c water, room temp

1/4 c heavy cream

1/2 c chicken broth

6 oz sharp cheddar, shredded

salt and pepper, to taste

METHOD

Steam broccoli florets.

Mix 1/2 cup broccoli with the cream cheese, 1/2 cup water, and the heavy cream. Blend until smooth.

Pour blended mixture into a large pot or saucepan. Add chicken broth, remaining broccoli and water.

Mix well over medium heat until simmering. Reduce heat slightly and add cheddar cheese.

Mix until the cheese melts and blends completely. Serve hot.

Per Serving: 244 Calories; 16g Fat (57.7% calories from fat); 35g Protein; 2g Carbohydrate; 0.4g Dietary Fiber.

BUTTERED SALMON & ONIONS

1g net carb per serving - 251 calories
Servings: 2

INGREDIENTS

6 oz salmon, fillets

1/4 c onion, sliced

1 tbsp unsalted butter

1 tsp coconut oil (sub MCT oil)

1/4 tsp lemon juice (sub zest)

1/4 tsp fresh dill, chopped fine

METHOD

Grill the salmon until tender. Cook a few onion pieces in a skillet until they reach a caramel color. Remove from heat, plate and set aside.

Add butter, coconut oil and lemon juice to the skillet. Heat until fully melted, blending well. Pour the sauce over the salmon, and top with onion and chopped dill.

Serve hot immediately, or store in the fridge (a great salad topper).

Per Serving: 251 Calories; 22g Fat (72.3% calories from fat); 17g Protein; 1g Carbohydrate; trace Dietary Fiber.

HOT GROUND BEEF & SOUR CREAM

1.6g net carbs per serving - 349 calories
Servings: 4

INGREDIENTS

12 oz ground beef

1/4 c onion, diced

2 tbsp water

Mexican spices, to taste

3 oz hot pepper cheese, shredded

4 tbsp sour cream

METHOD

Brown the ground beef and onions in a skillet.

Add a splash of water and taco seasoning (Check for carbs!) or preferred Mexican spices.

Mix and simmer 10 to 15 minutes.

Remove from heat and top with hot pepper cheese.

Stir lightly until just blended.

Top with a dollop (1 tbsp) of sour cream.

Per Serving: 349 Calories; 29g Fat (76.3% calories from fat); 20g Protein; 1.6g Carbohydrate; trace Dietary Fiber.

MOCK CURRY CHICKEN SOUP

2g net carbs per serving - 202 calories
Servings: 2

INGREDIENTS

2 tsp coconut oil (sub butter)

2 tsp curry powder

1/3 c heavy cream

1 c chicken broth

1 clove garlic, pressed

1 chicken bouillon cube

METHOD

Melt the coconut oil in a small saucepan over low heat.

Add curry powder and sauté a few minutes.

Add remaining ingredients and simmer, stirring to dissolve the bouillon completely.

Simmer 5 to 10 more minutes, remove from heat and serve immediately.

Per Serving: 202 Calories; 20g Fat (88.0% calories from fat); 3g Protein; 3g Carbohydrate; 1g Dietary Fiber.

Mock Curry Chicken Soup

PARMESAN CHICKEN BITES

0.5g net carbs per serving - 311 calories
Servings: 8 (about 2 oz of chicken)

INGREDIENTS

1 lb chicken breast, cooked

2 whole eggs

10 oz Parmesan cheese, grated

3 oz sharp cheddar cheese,
grated

1 tsp garlic powder

1/2 tsp sea salt

1/2 tsp black pepper

METHOD

Preheat your oven to 375 F.

Cut the chicken into 1-inch chunks.

Scramble the eggs and place into a bowl.

Mix the cheddar and Parmesan together in a
separate bowl.

Dip each piece of chicken into the scrambled egg.

Gently roll the chicken through the cheddar
Parmesan mix, fully coating all sides.

Place chicken bites on a greased baking sheet,
leaving space between each piece.

Sprinkle with garlic powder, sea salt and black
pepper.

Bake 15 to 20 minutes at 375 F, until golden and
crispy.

Per Serving: 311 Calories; 22g Fat (65.2% calories from fat); 26g Protein; 0.5 Carbohydrate; 0g Dietary Fiber.

DESSERTS

Blackberry Cream Cheese (pg 104)
with Chocolate Sauce (pg 51)

BLACKBERRY CREAM CHEESE

2g net carbs per serving - 205 calories
Servings: 4

INGREDIENTS

8 oz Neufchatel cheese, softened
(sub whipped)

vanilla extract, dash

stevia, to taste

1 c blackberries, fresh or frozen

METHOD

Mix softened cream cheese with vanilla, then add berries. Blend well.

Pour into a greased mug or ramekin, then pop into the freezer for 30 minutes.

Remove from freezer, warm the container in your hands, turn over and release onto a plate.

Also works with raspberries and blueberries (adjust your net carbs).

Optional: Cover in Chocolate Sauce (pg 51)!
(Add 1g net carb to your macros.)

TIP: *Make fruity fat bombs. Mash the berries into the mix, then drop spoonfuls on parchment paper. Freeze for 30 minutes. Pop your berry dots off the paper and store in a sealed container in the freezer.*

Per Serving: 205 Calories; 19g Fat (81.4% calories from fat); 22g Protein; 4g Carbohydrate; 2g Dietary Fiber.

CHOCOLATE ICE CREAM

2g net carbs per serving - 156 calories
Servings: 1

INGREDIENTS

3 tbsp heavy cream, whipped

2 tsp cocoa powder

stevia, to taste

vanilla extract, to taste

METHOD

Whip all ingredients together, pour into a small container, cover and freeze an hour or two.

TIP: *Make several servings of this recipe at once, then store individual portions inside small ramekins, wine glasses or mugs.*

Per Serving: 156 Calories; 15g Fat (90.0% calories from fat); 1g Protein; 3g Carbohydrate; 1g Dietary Fiber.

COCONUT SOUR CREAM

2g net carbs per serving - 145 calories
Servings: 1

INGREDIENTS

2 oz sour cream

2 tbsp shredded coconut, unsweetened

spritz of lime

METHOD

Toast coconut in a skillet over medium low heat. Watch carefully! Coconut shreds brown quickly.

Remove from heat and let cool a few minutes.

Sprinkle shredded coconut over sour cream, spritz with lime and eat.

Per Serving: 145 Calories; 14g Fat (87.0% calories from fat); 2g Protein; 3g Carbohydrate; 1g Dietary Fiber.

JELLO CHEESECAKE COOKIES

1g net carb per serving - 147 calories
Servings: 12 (1 cookie)

INGREDIENTS

6 oz Neufchatel cheese

4 tbsp unsalted butter, softened

1 whole egg

8 drops liquid stevia, or to taste

1/2 tsp vanilla extract

1/4 tsp almond extract (optional)

1/8 tsp sea salt

1 4-serving pkg sugar-free Jello,
Cheesecake (or any) flavor

1/2 tsp baking powder

1 c almond flour

METHOD

Preheat your oven to 325 F.

Soften cream cheese and butter. Beat the egg together with sweetener and extracts. Add cream cheese and butter. Mix in salt and one 4-serving packet of sugar-free Jello (gelatin, pudding, custard, etc.) Whisk baking powder into the almond flour.

Add this dry mix slowly to the wet mix a few tablespoons at a time. Blend well using a fork to form a slightly sticky dough.

Wrap dough and place into the fridge until firm, 30 minutes minimum, up to 12 hours.

Roll dough into one inch balls and place on a prepared baking sheet. Leave about one inch between each cookie. Use a fork, your thumb or the bottom of a glass to flatten the cookies. These do not spread during baking.

Thin, flat cookies are crispier, bake more quickly, and burn easily. Watch those last few minutes!

Bake 6 to 8 minutes at 325 F.

Remove from oven and allow to cool a few minutes before moving to a cooling rack.

Important: *Allow cookies to cool completely before serving or they crumble.*

Per Serving: 147 Calories; 14g Fat (84.9% calories from fat); 3g Protein; 2g Carbohydrate; 1g Dietary Fiber.

Jello Cheesecake Cookies

KETO CREAM CHEESE BALLS

1.8g net carbs per serving - 151 calories
Servings: 5 (2 balls)

INGREDIENTS

8 oz Neufchatel cheese, very cold

1 pkg sugar-free Jello (4 serving
size), any flavor (sub coconut
shreds or cocoa powder)

METHOD

Pour the Jello powder mix/coconut/cocoa into a bowl
or on a small plate, and set aside.

Cut the cream cheese into 10 small cubes and roll each
one in the dry powder/shreds.

Set the balls on a plate and cover with plastic wrap.

Refrigerate (or freeze) 30 minutes or until ready to serve.

TIP: *For better portion control, press slightly softened cream cheese into candy molds
and freeze. Pop out, then roll in your powder or mix.*

Per Serving: 151 Calories; 14g Fat (83.3% calories from fat); 17g Protein; 1.8g Carbohydrate; trace Dietary Fiber.

Keto Cream Cheese Balls

KETO MERINGUES

1g net carb per serving – 34 calories
Servings (10 cookies): 3

INGREDIENTS

5 egg whites

1 tsp lemon juice

1/8 tsp salt

1 c granulated stevia (or equiv)

1 1/4 tsp vanilla extract

1/4 tsp almond extract (optional)

METHOD

In a large bowl, beat egg whites, lemon juice and salt until foamy. Add the stevia slowly and continue beating until fully mixed. Add vanilla and almond extracts, beating until glossy and medium-stiff peaks form.

Pipe (or spoon) mixture into 30 mounds on a parchment paper-lined baking sheet. Bake 5 to 10 minutes at 300 F.

Lower oven temperature to 250 F and bake 20 more minutes. Lower oven temperature again to 200 F and bake another 20 minutes. Turn off the oven heat.

Let meringues cool in the oven 1 to 2 hours.

Per Serving: 34 Calories; trace Fat (0.1% calories from fat); 6g Protein; 1g Carbohydrate; trace Dietary Fiber.

LEMON CHEESECAKE BITES

1g net carb per serving - 210 calories
Servings: 6

INGREDIENTS

1/4 c coconut oil, melted

4 tbsp unsalted butter, softened

4 oz Neufchatel cheese, softened

1 tbsp lemon zest, finely grated

1 tsp lemon juice

lemon extract, optional

stevia, to taste

METHOD

Set some lemon zest aside for a garnish.

Blend all ingredients with a hand mixer until smooth.

Pour into cupcake liners, tins or molds. You may also use a small dish and cut into squares just before serving.

Freeze until firm, at least a few hours, preferably overnight.

Sprinkle with more lemon zest before serving.

Per Serving: 210 Calories; 21g Fat (90.6% calories from fat); 7g Protein; 1g Carbohydrate; trace Dietary Fiber.

Keto Meringues

NUT BARK

2 net carbs per serving - 151 calories
Servings: 12

INGREDIENTS

1 oz pistachio nuts (about 25 nuts),
toasted and chopped

1/3 c unsweetened coconut flakes

3 1/2 oz dark chocolate, 85%

1/2 c coconut butter

1/2 tsp vanilla extract

1/4 tsp almond extract, optional

10 drops liquid stevia

1/4 tsp sea salt, coarsely ground

METHOD

Preheat the oven to 350 F.

Toast shelled pistachios and coconut flakes on a lined baking sheet.

Toast 5 to 8 minutes, tossing once or twice to prevent burning. Remove from oven and set aside to cool.

In a double boiler, melt coconut butter and chocolate over low heat. Add in cocoa powder, stevia and salt, stirring gently until mixed.

Remove from heat. Stir in vanilla and almond extracts.

Pour onto a parchment paper-lined baking sheet. (You may also use a piece of plastic wrap on a baking sheet, a flexible cutting mat, or silicone chocolate bar molds.)

While chocolate is still warm, sprinkle with toasted coconut flakes and roasted nuts.

Let cool, then break apart.

Per Serving: 151 Calories; 15g Fat (86.0% calories from fat); 1g Protein; 4g Carbohydrate; 2g Dietary Fiber.

Nut Bark

RASPBERRIES & MASCARPONE

1g net carb per serving - 105 calories
Servings: 1

INGREDIENTS

3 tbsp Mascarpone cheese

vanilla extract, dash

stevia, to taste

10 whole raspberries, fresh or frozen

METHOD

Mix cheese with vanilla and stevia,
then add berries (whole or mashed).

Also works with blackberries and blueberries.

TIP: *Add unsweetened coconut shreds if you're craving crunch.*

Per Serving: 105 Calories; 10g Fat (86.5% calories from fat); 1g Protein; 2g Carbohydrate; 1g Dietary Fiber.

VANILLA CHOCOLATE MOUSSE

0.6g net carbs per serving - 251 calories
Servings: 4

INGREDIENTS

2 oz unsalted butter, softened

1 tbsp stevia, or to taste

1/2 tsp vanilla extract

2 oz Neufchatel cheese

1 tbsp cocoa powder

3 oz heavy cream, whipped

METHOD

Soften butter and combine with sweetener and vanilla, stirring until completely blended.

Add cream cheese and continue blending until smooth. Add the cocoa powder (slowly) as you blend.

Whip the heavy cream until still peaks form, then gradually fold it into the chocolate mixture.

Spoon into small glasses or containers and refrigerate for 30 minutes.

TIP: *Pour mixture into a small baking dish or pan, freeze, then cut into cubes. Or, pour into ice cube tray compartments.*

Per Serving: 251 Calories; 26g Fat (93.4% calories from fat); 3g Protein; 1g Carbohydrate; trace Dietary Fiber.

Vanilla Chocolate Mousse

VANILLA CINNAMON MASCARPONE

0g net carbs per serving - 194 calories
Servings: 1

INGREDIENTS

3 tbsp Mascarpone cheese

vanilla extract

dash cinnamon

stevia, to taste

METHOD

This is a rare, absolutely zero carb dessert.

Mascarpone isn't particularly flavorful served alone, but it's 100% fat and we love that.

Mix all ingredients together until well-blended.

Chill 30 minutes, or until set.

TIP: *Add a sprinkle of cocoa or espresso powder to the mix without adding carbs.*

Per Serving: 194 Calories; 20g Fat (95.2% calories from fat); 2g Protein; 0g Carbohydrate; 0g Dietary Fiber.

VANILLA ICE CREAM

1.6g net carbs per serving - 197 calories
Servings: 1

INGREDIENTS

1/4 c heavy cream, whipped

stevia, to taste

vanilla extract, dash

METHOD

Add all ingredients to a bowl and whip until still peaks form.

Place in the freezer for 30 minutes to an hour.

TIP: *This recipe is even easier to make using an inexpensive mini frother inside a small ramekin or coffee mug.*

Per Serving: 197 Calories; 21g Fat (96.6% calories from fat); 0g Protein; 1.6g Carbohydrate; 0g Dietary Fiber.

7-DAY
INDUCTION
MEAL PLAN

MONDAY

Breakfast	**Snack 1**	**Lunch**	**Snack 2**	**Dinner**
2 sm tomatoes 1 tbsp olive oil 2 lg eggs 2 oz sausage	1 stalk celery 2 tbsp cream cheese	6 oz salmon 2 c lettuce leaves 2 tbsp sherry vinegar	1 oz deli roast beef (any deli meat) 1 oz cheddar cheese slice *rolled up* (or any type of cheese)	6 oz chicken, cooked 2 c spinach 1/4 c cucumber slices 1/2 avocado 2 tbsp sherry vinegar
548 Calories; 47g Fat (76.5% calories from fat); 21g Protein; 11g Carbohydrate; 5g Dietary Fiber.	103 Calories; 9g Fat (83.4% calories from fat); 2g Protein; 2g Carbohydrate; 1g Dietary Fiber.	214 Calories; 6g Fat (25.8% calories from fat); 35g Protein; 4g Carbohydrate; 1g Dietary Fiber.	164 Calories; 10g Fat (58.2% calories from fat); 15g Protein; 2g Carbohydrate; 0g Dietary Fiber.	451 Calories; 35g Fat (65.4% calories from fat); 25g Protein; 16g Carbohydrate; 12g Dietary Fiber.

Notes

MACROS

1480 Calories – 16g Net Carbs: 106g Fat (64.3% calories from fat); 99g Protein; 35g Carbohydrate; 19g Dietary Fiber.

TUESDAY

Breakfast	Snack 1	Lunch	Snack 2	Dinner
5 oz salmon, smoked 2 tbsp cream cheese 1/4 cucumber, cut into sticks	5 lg olives, black 1 oz feta cheese	6 oz chicken 2 c lettuce 5 lg radishes 1/2 avocado 2 tbsp ranch salad dressing	1 med tomato 1 oz cheddar cheese	6 oz steak 1 c broccoli 1 c cauliflower 2 tbsp olive oil
271 Calories; 14g Fat (48.7% calories from fat); 30g Protein; 3g Carbohydrate; 1g Dietary Fiber.	100 Calories; 8g Fat (74.9% calories from fat); 4g Protein; 2g Carbohydrate; 1g Dietary Fiber.	563 Calories; 51g Fat (74.4% calories from fat); 26g Protein; 13g Carbohydrate; 10g Dietary Fiber.	136 Calories; 10g Fat (61.8% calories from fat); 8g Protein; 5g Carbohydrate; 2g Dietary Fiber.	657 Calories; 57g Fat (77.5% calories from fat); 28g Protein; 9g Carbohydrate; 5g Dietary Fiber.

Notes

MACROS

1727 Calories – 13g Net Carbs: 136g Fat (70.9% calories from fat); 97g Protein; 31g Carbohydrate; 18g Dietary Fiber.

WEDNESDAY

Breakfast	Snack 1	Lunch	Snack 2	Dinner
1/4 c bell pepper, chopped 2 lg eggs 1 oz hot pepper cheese 4 tbsp salsa	2 celery stalks 2 tbsp ranch salad dressing	5 oz ground beef, cooked 1 oz cheddar cheese 1 sm tomato 1/2 avocado 1 lettuce leaf	1/2 c bell pepper, sliced 2 tbsp ranch salad dressing	6 oz chicken 1 c green beans 1 tbsp butter
286 Calories; 19g Fat (60.1% calories from fat); 21g Protein; 8g Carbohydrate; 2g Dietary Fiber.	125 Calories; 16g Fat (89.9% calories from fat); 2g Protein; 2g Carbohydrate; 0g Dietary Fiber.	738 Calories; 55g Fat (74.8% calories from fat); 34g Protein; 14g Carbohydrate; 9g Dietary Fiber.	133 Calories; 16g Fat (84.0% calories from fat); 2g Protein; 5g Carbohydrate; 1g Dietary Fiber	400 Calories; 31g Fat (69.0% calories from fat); 23g Protein; 8g Carbohydrate; 4g Dietary Fiber.

Notes

MACROS

1682 Calories – 20g Net Carbs: 137g Fat (73.4% calories from fat); 82g Protein; 36g Carbohydrate; 16g Dietary

THURSDAY

Breakfast	Snack 1	Lunch	Snack 2	Dinner
2 lg eggs 2 bacon slices 1 med tomato 2 tbsp Parmesan cheese, grated	2 oz cheddar cheese	5 oz chicken, roasted 2 c spinach 2 tbsp ranch salad dressing	1/4 c cucumber slices 2 oz Monterey jack cheese	6 oz fish fillets 1 c broccoli, florets 2 tbsp butter
289 Calories; 19g Fat (60.5% calories from fat); 22g Protein; 7g Carbohydrate; 2g Dietary Fiber.	228 Calories; 19g Fat (74.0% calories from fat); 14g Protein; 1g Carbohydrate; 0g Dietary Fiber.	346 Calories; 29g Fat (74.0% calories from fat); 21g Protein; 5g Carbohydrate; 2g Dietary Fiber.	219 Calories; 17g Fat (70.9% calories from fat); 14g Protein; 2g Carbohydrate; 1g Dietary Fiber.	363 Calories; 24g Fat (60.1% calories from fat); 33g Protein; 4g Carbohydrate; 2g Dietary Fiber.

Notes

MACROS

1445 Calories – 10g Net Carbs: 108g Fat (67.5% calories from fat); 104g Protein; 17g Carbohydrate; 7g Dietary Fiber.

FRIDAY

Breakfast

5 oz ground beef
1 tbsp olive oil
1/2 c bell pepper,
chopped
2 tbsp onion,
chopped
1/4 c cheddar
cheese, shredded

698 Calories;
61g Fat (78.2%
calories from fat);
32g Protein;
6g Carbohydrate;
2g Dietary Fiber.

Notes

Snack 1

1/2 med zucchini,
cut into sticks
2 oz provolone
cheese

213 Calories;
15g Fat (64.4%
calories from fat);
16g Protein;
3g Carbohydrate;
1g Dietary Fiber.
.

Lunch

6 oz turkey breast
cutlets
2 c spinach
1/2 avocado
2 tbsp Italian salad
dressing

482 Calories;
32g Fat (56.1%
calories from fat);
40g Protein;
16g Carbohydrate;
11g Dietary Fiber.

Snack 2

1 celery stalk
2 tbsp cream
cheese

103 Calories;
9g Fat (85.0%
calories from fat);
2g Protein;
2g Carbohydrate;
0g Dietary Fiber.

Dinner

7 oz pork chops
1/2 c Brussels
sprouts
1 tbsp butter
2 c lettuce
2 tbsp sherry
vinegar

451 Calories;
31g Fat (62.1%
calories from fat);
34g Protein;
10g Carbohydrate;
4g Dietary Fiber.

MACROS

1947 Calories – 19g Net Carbs: 146g Fat (67.6% calories from fat); 123g Protein; 37g Carbohydrate; 18g Dietary Fiber.

SATURDAY

Breakfast	Snack 1	Lunch	Snack 2	Dinner
1 sm tomato	5 lg radishes	4 oz tuna	1/2 med cucumber,	5 oz ground beef
1/2 avocado	(or 1/2 med	1 1/2 celery stalk	sliced	1 oz cheddar
4 oz prosciutto	cucumber)	1/2 c bell pepper,	1 oz cheddar	cheese
2 tbsp butter or	1 oz Gouda	chopped	cheese	1 sm tomato
mayo	cheese	2 tbsp mayo		1 c lettuce
				2 tbsp ranch salad
				dressing

Breakfast	Snack 1	Lunch	Snack 2	Dinner
436 Calories;	106 Calories;	390 Calories;	134 Calories;	698 Calories;
28g Fat (55.1%	8g Fat (67.3%	29g Fat (65.8%	10g Fat (63.1%	57g Fat (77.7%
calories from fat);	calories from fat);	calories from fat);	calories from fat);	calories from fat);
35g Protein;	7g Protein;	28g Protein;	8g Protein;	34g Protein;
20g Carbohydrate;	1g Carbohydrate;	6g Carbohydrate;	5g Carbohydrate;	7g Carbohydrate;
10g Dietary Fiber.	trace Dietary Fiber.	1g Dietary Fiber.	1g Dietary Fiber.	3g Dietary Fiber.

Notes

MACROS

1764 Calories – 24g Net Carbs: 132g Fat (67.8% calories from fat); 112g Protein; 40g Carbohydrate; 16g Dietary Fiber.

SUNDAY

Breakfast	Snack 1	Lunch	Snack 2	Dinner
1 sm tomato	5 lg radishes	1/2 med cucumber,	1 celery stalk	5 oz ground beef
1/2 avocado	(or 1/2 med	sliced	2 tbsp cream	1 oz cheddar
4 oz prosciutto	cucumber)	1 oz cheddar	cheese	cheese
2 tbsp butter or	1 oz Gouda	cheese		1 sm tomato
mayo	cheese	2 tbsp mayo		1 c lettuce
				2 tbsp ranch salad
				dressing

436 Calories;	106 Calories;	366 Calories	134 Calories;	698 Calories;
28g Fat (55.1%	8g Fat (67.3%	31g Fat (56.1%	10g Fat (63.1%	55g Fat (77.7%
calories from fat);	calories from fat);	calories from fat);	calories from fat);	calories from fat);
35g Protein;	7g Protein;	40g Protein;	8g Protein;	34g Protein;
20g Carbohydrate;	1g Carbohydrate;	16g Carbohydrate;	5g Carbohydrate;	7g Carbohydrate;
10g Dietary Fiber.	trace Dietary Fiber.	11g Dietary Fiber.	1g Dietary Fiber.	3g Dietary Fiber.

Notes

MACROS

1740 Calories – 23g Net Carbs: 131g Fat (67.8% calories from fat); 112g Protein; 35g Carbohydrate; 16g Dietary Fiber.

RESOURCES

ZERO CARB FOOD LIST

Finding foods with zero carbs isn't hard. Use this list, read package labels carefully and prepare to be pleasantly surprised at all your options.

The list of low carb foods is HUGE. Zero carb foods are more limited, especially in the fruit and veggie areas. There are still over 100 foods with no carbs, so it's easy to create a large variety of meals.

Using this List

Technically speaking, fats are the only foods that are completely zero carb. Even proteins like meat and seafood have trace amounts of carbs.

The foods on this list have very minor amounts of net carbs (fractions of a gram). These foods are so close to zero, most low carbers consider them zero carb foods. Legally, these are zero carb. However, we've revealed all the hidden carbs in exact amounts.

The "almost zero carb foods" are a bit higher, but a single serving is still under 1g net carb. Please track your servings carefully. Trace amounts of net carb grams add up quickly.

Healthy Fats

Since most of your calories come from fat, it's important to include healthy choices, like Omega 3 fats.

Animal fats (including lard)
Avocado oil
Coconut Oil — High in medium chain triglyceride (MCT) fatty acids. MCT fat is used for immediate energy, metabolized differently and not stored.
Fish oil
Grass-fed butter

Olive oil
MCT Oil — Easy to absorb and digest, converts into energy faster than other oils, ignites your body's metabolic rate and helps maintain healthy cholesterol levels.
Walnut oil

Less Healthy Oils

Full-fat Mayonnaise (check each label)
Sesame oil

Zero Carb Meat

High in protein and vitamins, most natural meats have no carbs.

Packaged, cured and processed meats (sausage, hot dogs, deli meat, bacon, etc.) have some net carb grams due to added flavoring, preservatives or starchy binders. Please check each label.

Beef
Lamb
Pork
Veal
Fowl (turkey, chicken, duck, goose, hen, quail)
Organ meats (brains, tongue, liver, heart)
Game meats (venison, bison, caribou, elk)
Exotic meats (ostrich, emu)

Zero Carb Seafood

Most fresh (unprocessed) seafood is zero carb.

Bass
Cod
Flounder
Haddock
Halibut

Salmon
Sardine
Sole
Tilapia
Tuna
Trout

These options have trace carbs:

Crab
Lobster
Shrimp
Squid

These options have a bit more:

Clams (0.35g net carbs per clam)
Oysters (0.35g net carbs per oyster)
Mussels (0.38g net carbs per mussel)

Almost Zero Carb Fruit & Veggies

Serving size: 1/2 cup

Spinach (chopped), 0.2g
Arugula, 0.2g
Lettuce, 0.25g
Parsley (chopped), 0.4g
Avocado (sliced or chunks), 0.5g
Radish (sliced), 0.5g
Bok Choy (chopped), 0.7g
Celery (chopped), 0.8g

Serving size: 1/4 cup

Cabbage, 0.5g
Garlic (1 small clove), 0.5g
Mushrooms (sliced), 0.5g
Pokeberry Shoots, 0.5g
Asparagus, (3 pieces) 0.6g

Cauliflower, (chopped) 0.7g
Coconut (unsweetened, shredded), 0.7g
(check each label, brands differ)

Raspberries, 0.7g
Yellow Squash (sliced), 0.7g
Broccoli (chopped), 0.8g
Cucumber (sliced), 0.9g

Almost Zero Carb Eggs

Eggs, 0.2g to 1g per egg (check the carton)

Eggs are almost zero carb, ranging from 0.2g to 1g net carb per egg. Organic, free-range, cage-free, etc. eggs have larger yolks, and are lower in net carbs.

Eggs are also very versatile: fried, scrambled, omelets, quiche, hard-boiled, deviled and of course, egg salad.

Almost Zero Carb Dairy

Most heavy cream brands have some net carbs per tablespoon, even if the packaging claims "0g carbs."

Heavy Cream has 0.4g net carbs per tablespoon.

Half-and-Half has 0.2g to 1g net carb per tablespoon.

Check labels carefully. Each brand is very different.

Almost Zero Carb Cheese

Most sources round up to the nearest net carb. Your list includes every single fraction of a carb.

Most natural, unprocessed cheeses (no added flavors or ingredients) are 0g to 1g net carb per serving.

Hard cheeses are the lowest in net carbs; softer, creamy cheeses are higher.

Mascarpone cheese is 100% fat and absolutely zero carb.

When in doubt, check each label.

Serving size: 1 oz = 1/4 cup grated

Mascarpone, 0g
Brie, 0.1g
Camembert, 0.1g
Gruyère, 0.1g

Monterey, 0.1g
Neufchatel, 0.1g to 0.8g
Cheddar, 0.3g
Muenster, 0.3g
Edam, 0.4g
Fontina, 0.4g
Mexican blend, 0.5g
Blue, 0.6g
Goats, 0.6g
Gouda, 0.6g
Mozzarella, 0.6
Provolone, 0.6g
Colby, 0.7g
Havarti, 0.7g
Ricotta, 0.8g
Asiago, 0.9g
Parmesan, 0.9g

Zero Carb Seasoning

Simply put, flavoring no carb foods makes meals much more palatable.

Salt and Pepper
Red Wine Vinegar
Most Hot Sauces
Spices and Seasonings (check the label)
Yellow Mustard
Fresh Herbs

DIY Zero Carb Spice Mixes

Mix ingredients in a jar, shake, cover and store in your spice rack up to 6 months.

Chili

2 tbsp paprika
2 tsp ground oregano
1 1/4 tsp ground cumin
1 1/4 tsp garlic powder

1 1/4 tsp cayenne pepper
3/4 tsp onion powder, optional

Curry

2 tbsp whole coriander seeds
1 tsp cumin seeds
1/2 tsp whole mustard seeds
1 piece of cinnamon bark
10 whole cloves
1 tsp ground turmeric
1 tsp ground cardamom
1 tsp ground cayenne

Italian

1 tbsp dried basil
1 tbsp dried oregano
1 tbsp dried rosemary
1 tbsp dried marjoram
1 tbsp dried thyme
1 tbsp dried savory
1 tsp red pepper flakes

Pumpkin Spice

4 tsp ground cinnamon
2 tsp ground ginger
1 tsp ground allspice
1 tsp ground nutmeg

Ranch

1/4 cup (6g) dried parsley
1 tbsp dried dill weed
1 tbsp garlic powder
1 tbsp onion powder
1/2 tsp basil leaf
1/2 tsp ground pepper

Zero Carb Sweeteners

Companies advertise aspartame, sucralose, saccharine and stevia as no carb sugar substitutes. However, the powder and granular versions usually contain trace amounts of carbohydrate fillers.

Preferred Sweeteners

Liquid de-bittered stevia, erythritol and xylitol are the preferred, natural zero carb sweeteners. Liquid sucralose is also zero carb, but not your healthiest choice.

Zero Carb Beverages

Water, Sparkling or Still
Club Soda
Unsweetened, Flavored Seltzer or
Sparkling Water
Coffee (preferably decaf)
Tea (preferably decaf)
(some flavored teas have net carbs)
Diet Soda
(check the artificial sweetener)

Zero Carb Alcohol

During your fasting plan, do not drink! Adding 1 to 2 oz of wine/liquor to a sauce or marinade is acceptable.

You may be knocked out of ketosis for several hours (or days) after drinking. You'll burn alcohol before fat for fuel. Once you've metabolized the alcohol, you'll return to fat-burning.

Gin
Rum (unflavored)
Vodka (unflavored)
Whiskey
Tequila
Scotch

Almost Zero Carb Wine

Most wine has 3 to 5g net carbs per 6 oz serving. These net carb stats are averages. Nutrition and net carbs in wine remains somewhat of a mystery. Check each vineyard's website.

Important: Serving size is 3 oz!

Red

Pinot Noir, 1.7g
Merlot, 1.85g
Cabernet, 1.9g

White

Champagne/Sparkling, 0.75g
Pinot Grigio, 1.6g
Pinot Gris, 1.6g
Chardonnay, 1.85g

Almost Zero Carb Beer

Most beer is too high carb to be enjoyed on a regular basis. There are a few manageable choices available, but only after you've completed the fast.

Serving size: 12 oz

Greens Trailblazer, 0.5g
Budweiser Select, 1.9g
DAB Low Carb, 2g
Sleeman Clear, 2g
Rolling Rock Green Light, 2.4g
Miller Genuine Draft Light, 2.4g
Molson Ultra, 2.5g
Labatt Sterling, 2.5g

Bacon Wrapped Asparagus (pg 65)
with poached eggs and
Spicy Keto Mayo

The Usual Disclaimer

Low Carbe Diem is not a medical company or organization. *The Almost Zero Carb Fat Fast* recipes, info about healthy eating and nutrition stats are intended for informational purposes only.

We are not doctors, nutritionists or medical professionals. The information in the *Almost Zero Carb Fat Fast* and the information on the website **LowCarbeDiem.com** is not meant to be given as medical advice.

We are simply sharing successful strategies and resources for low carb/keto ways of eating.

Before starting any diet, please discuss the changes with your doctor and follow all professional medical advice, seeking help if needed.

This fat fast is very aggressive. If you have any medical conditions such as diabetes, you must inform your doctor and only follow the fat fast under medical supervision. As with any dietary change, medications may need adjusting.

Thanks for your support and excellent feedback.

Breakfast Sausage Balls (pg 34)
and Avocado Bacon Mash (pg 50)

About the Author

Ann Marie Moore discovered the joy of keto by accident, during a wild attempt to "lose those last 10 pounds." She knew low carb diets worked quickly for fat loss, but she never expected to feel so energetic, motivated or focused.

Blending culinary passion with her Bachelor of Fine Arts and Master of Liberal Arts degrees, Ann Marie created *Low Carbe Diem* in 2012. The simple low carb blog slowly grew into a top food website, with millions of readers visiting each month for easy keto recipes, hot new shortcuts, safe cheats and easy gourmet meals.

Today, Ann Marie creates keto recipes and meal plans, writes almost zero carb cookbooks and articles, shares simple low carb solutions and helps others discover the life-changing effects of nutritional ketosis.

She lives in Philadelphia, PA with her Mini Goldendoodle, Coco. She enjoys painting low carb veggies, long wheat-less walks on the beach, grass-fed butter and bacon.

Visit her at LowCarbeDiem.com.

Printed in Great Britain
by Amazon